Bescherelle

anglais

les exercices

Michèle Malavieille

Agrégée de l'Université

Mireille Quivy

Agrégée de l'Université
Maître de conférences à l'université de Rouen

Wilfrid Rotgé

Agrégé de l'Université
Professeur de linguistique anglaise
à l'université Paris-Ouest Nanterre La Défense

ÉDITION : Barthélemy de Lesseps

CONCEPTION GRAPHIQUE : Anne Gallet ▲ MISE EN PAGE : Isabelle Vacher

© Hatier, Paris, février 2009 - ISSN : 2101-1249 - ISBN : 978-2-218-93450-6

mode d'emploi

Un outil complet

• Cet ouvrage propose un travail d'appropriation, de consolidation et de réflexion permettant la maîtrise de la langue anglaise.

• Il a été conçu comme un **complément de l'ouvrage** *la Grammaire anglaise*, dans la même collection **Bescherelle**, mais il peut s'utiliser indépendamment de celle-ci.

• Les exercices proposés sont variés et précisément adaptés aux points de langue abordés. Tous les points clés de la grammaire anglaise y sont explorés.

Un outil progressif

• Les exercices ne sont pas organisés en niveaux de difficulté, afin de ne pas figer la dynamique de l'entraînement. En revanche, une progression existe, du plus simple au plus difficile, à l'intérieur de chaque exercice et d'un exercice à l'autre dans chaque point de grammaire abordé.

• Une révision préliminaire peut être nécessaire. Il suffit de se reporter pour chaque chapitre aux paragraphes correspondants de la *Grammaire*. Les renvois à ces paragraphes, indiqués à l'aide du symbole §, permettent des révisions plus ciblées.

Un outil pour tous les publics

L'ouvrage s'adresse à un large public – lycéens, étudiants, adultes – et peut être utilisé en toute autonomie. Tous les exercices sont intégralement corrigés. Il est conseillé de les faire en temps limité et de ne consulter les corrigés que pour valider les réponses.

• Cet ouvrage de la collection **Bescherelle** est associé à des compléments numériques : un ensemble d'exercices interactifs supplémentaires sur les principales difficultés de la langue anglaise.
• Pour y accéder, connectez-vous au site **www.bescherelle.com**.
Inscrivez-vous en sélectionnant le titre. Il vous suffira ensuite d'indiquer un mot clé issu de l'ouvrage pour accéder librement aux ressources diverses liées à la collection **Bescherelle** en anglais.

sommaire

Le groupe verbal

Verbes prépositionnels §9-13

1 Traduisez ces phrases dont les verbes sont prépositionnels ou non.

1. Il n'a pas encore répondu à ma lettre.
2. Il cherche ses clefs.
3. Il manque de courage.
4. Hier, nous avons attendu un taxi vingt minutes.
5. As-tu téléphoné à Judith ?
6. Que penses-tu de ça ?
7. J'ai pensé à ce que tu as dit.
8. Elle se souvient de lui.
9. Est-ce que tu lui fais confiance ?

2 Traduisez ces phrases.

1. Elle joue merveilleusement du violon.
2. Qu'est-ce que tu regardes comme ça ?
3. Il entra dans la pièce sans frapper.
4. Vous n'avez pas traité *(deal with)* le sujet.
5. As-tu besoin d'un dictionnaire ?
6. J'ai assez d'argent pour payer le repas.
7. Nous discuterons de ce sujet plus tard.

Verbes à particules §14-16

3 Complétez ces phrases avec une particule.

1. Go…! Leave me alone! WAY
2. The plane took … on time. Off
3. Don't forget to take your passport … when you leave.
4. When can I get my money …? Back
5. You're cold. Why don't you put … a cardigan?
6. We usually eat … *(aller au restaurant)* on Friday evening.
7. Don't stay here, move … .
8. He says he'll do the kitchen … when he is on holiday.
9. Has he given … smoking yet?
10. Do come … and see us one evening.

4 Complétez ces phrases avec la particule qui convient, puis traduisez les verbes ainsi obtenus.

1. Could you call … at the post office on your way home tonight?
2. The match was called … due to the bad weather conditions.
3. You'll get into trouble if you carry … like that!
4. You'll have to cut … on luxuries if you want to go on that cruise.
5. I ended … by telling him the whole story.
6. How is he getting … with his wife now?
7. They seem to be pretty close: they always hang … together.
8. Don't put … going to the dentist's if you have a toothache.
9. We'd better hurry: our time is running … .
10. Techno doesn't turn me … .

5 Remplacez le verbe en italiques par le verbe entre parenthèses plus une particule.

EXEMPLE : The fire-brigade soon *extinguished* the fire. (put)
▷ The fire-brigade soon put the fire out.

1. Five prisoners have *escaped* and are on the run. (break)
2. Several experiments have been *conducted* in that field. (carry)
3. The news *spread* that more people would be made redundant. (get)
4. The exam was easy enough. Most candidates *passed*. (get)
5. His book was *refused* by four publishers. (turn)
6. He *entered suddenly* and switched off the television. (burst)
7. Her interest in him seems to have *lost in power*. (wear)
8. He *proved* to be an excellent cook. (turn)

2 | Les verbes *be, have, do*

Be et *have*   § 19-27

6 Remplacez *'s* par *is* ou *has* lorsque c'est possible.

1. That's what he's just said.
2. He's had a long chat with her at Paul's and it's all sorted out.
3. It's got a certain reputation.
4. She thinks she's always right.
5. What's the matter with her? She's always cold.
6. He's agreed to her proposal.
7. He's said to have married twice.

7 Employez *have* au temps indiqué et à la forme qui convient.
Utilisez *have got* lorsque cette forme est possible.

1. ... you ... a good time? (prétérit)
2. She ... not ... a car. (présent)
3. I ... never ... so much to do. (*present perfect*)
4. Yesterday they ... dinner at 9. (prétérit)
5. "... you really ... to go now?" "Yes, I'm afraid I ... to." (présent)
6. I ... not usually ... a drink before dinner. (présent)
7. We had free tickets: we ... not ... to pay. (prétérit)
8. This ring is very dear to me: I ... it for years. (*present perfect*)
9. We couldn't go out in the rain: we ... not ... an umbrella. (prétérit)
10. We ... plenty of time: we ... not ... to hurry. (présent)

8 Traduisez.

1. Il aura quatorze ans en décembre.
2. Tu devrais avoir honte.
3. Il a les yeux bleus.
4. As-tu faim ou soif ?
5. Nous avons reçu beaucoup de visiteurs cet été.
6. Vous en reprendrez ?
7. Vous vous êtes bien amusés ?
8. Elles ont le même âge.
9. J'ai tout ce qu'il me faut.
10. Ça a quelle hauteur ?

« Il y a », « il y avait », « il y aura »   § 20, 66

9 Soulignez les formes que l'on peut traduire
par « il y a/il y avait/il y aura... », puis traduisez les phrases.

1. I'm not new; I've done it for years.
2. Winning is an important word. There is one that achieves what he wanted to do and there are hundreds of thousands that fail.
3. Now they were twenty and they had not seen each other for years.
4. It has been a long time since you came to town.
5. Twenty years ago tonight I dined here with my friend.
6. The building teemed with *(grouillait de)* cats. There were even a couple of dogs... There were many complaints.
7. I found a bag of money 52 years ago. I took that bag and used it to make more money.
8. The school has only been here a hundred years.

10 Traduisez.

1. Il y a un restaurant indien dans ma rue. J'y ai dîné il y a trois jours.
2. « Quand as-tu vu ta mère pour la dernière fois *(last)* ? – Il y a presque deux ans. »
3. Il y a vingt-huit ans qu'il est député *(an M.P.)*.
4. « Il y a combien de temps que tu as visité Londres ? – Cinq ou six ans. »
5. Il y a neuf mille kilomètres de Paris à San Francisco.
6. Il y a huit ans que je le connais.
7. Il y a combien jusqu'au prochain arrêt de bus ?
8. Il y a vingt ans, c'était différent.

Do (does/did) de reprise   § 31

11 Complétez ces phrases avec *do (does/don't/doesn't)* ou *did (didn't)*.

1. "I punched him in the nose once or twice, I think." "You think?" "I guess I ..."
2. "So you like that, ... you?" "Well, yes," she answered. "I must say I ..."
3. He inquired whether they had enjoyed themselves. "Yes, we ...," Grace replied.
4. "I overheard you talking about those books." "Oh? You ..., ... you?"
5. "You knew all the time she was ill, ... you?"

6. "Would you like me to explain? " "Please ..."

7. You never know what to expect from these sorts of things, ... you?

8. "You gave him the address, ... you?"

9. "I don't suppose you phoned him, ... you?"

10. "What right have they got to send me this?" "I don't know, I really ..."

12 Traduisez.

1. Je te l'ai dit, non ?

2. Vous ne connaissez pas l'homme, moi oui.

3. « Je pourrais obtenir un meilleur travail. – J'en doute. – Ah oui ? Pourquoi ? »

4. « Il vit ici maintenant. – Ah oui ? Je ne savais pas. »

5. « Il m'a dit quelque chose sur toi. – Il a fait ça ? Et qu'est-ce que c'était ? »

6. Je ne comprends pas pourquoi il est venu si tôt. Et toi ?

7. « Je t'avais dit d'utiliser l'ordinateur. – C'est ce que j'ai fait ! »

8. Nous savons où c'est. Et vous ?

Formes du présent § 34-41

13 Mettez les verbes suivants à la troisième personne du singulier du présent simple, forme affirmative.

run • work • pay • lie • cry • catch • laugh • go • hurry • pass • relax

14 Mettez ces phrases à la forme interrogative.

1. She gets up at 6. ▷ What time …?
2. Yes, it's raining very hard. ▷ …?
3. I'm reading *Dark Water*. ▷ What …?
4. Yes, she agrees with you. ▷ …?
5. No, I don't like sweets. ▷ …?
6. He's coming back tomorrow. ▷ When …?
7. She leaves home at 7 every day. ▷ When …?
8. They do nothing. ▷ What …?
9. Yes, she knows him. ▷ …?
10. I'm waiting for my change. ▷ What …?

Présent simple ou en *be* + V-*ing* § 37-47

15 Mettez le verbe entre parenthèses au présent simple ou en *be* + V-*ing*.

1. Did I hear you all right or (dream/I)?
2. I hardly ever (dream) of him and yet I (love) him.
3. You can't see her now. She (have) a bath.
4. You (look) sad. What (think/you) about?
5. "(write/you) to him tonight?" "Yes, I always (write) to him on June 17th."
6. This film (come) to the local cinema next week. (want/you) to see it?
7. Mark, whose forty-fourth birthday (come up), (think) of himself as a lucky man.
8. When people (say) the subway (frighten) them they (not be) silly.
9. "They (not have) cars like we (do), (do/they)?" said my mother. I said, "What (talk/you) about, Mom, of course the British (have) cars."
"What about the food? Should I bring some with me?"
"Mom, you (come) to London, you (not trek) through Katmandu."
10. "You (look) so young!" "I'm twenty-two." "Then this year in America, (look/you) for work there?" "I (actually not look) for anything. I (pass through)."

16 Soulignez les verbes au présent puis classez-les dans les grilles ci-dessous.

1. This thing weighs a ton. I can't lift it.

2. I am just going round the corner. Your tea is ready. Don't feed the cat.

3. "Where do you shop?" "Sainsbury's."

4. We begin the journey home. The snow is falling heavily. The temperature is dropping.

5. "It's a pity you don't like her. You don't, do you?" "Why are you asking?"

6. He sits on his bar-stool and I reckon he's thinking the same things I'm thinking.

7. Gus ties his laces, rises, yawns and begins to walk slowly to the door. He stops, looks down, and shakes his foot.

8. "I really am sorry. I'm always doing this." "Oh, it doesn't matter."

9. Nobody in this house is speaking to you ever again.

10. Don't talk to me. I don't care. It doesn't bother me. I don't know why you're all being so unsociable.

11. "You say 'bloody'," she said to Larry. "You say it all the time. You're always saying 'bloody this' and 'bloody that.'"

---

le présent simple

Il est utilisé :
- pour énoncer une caractéristique : …
- pour relater des actions successives : …
- pour décrire une habitude : …
- pour décrire une scène à la manière d'une indication scénique : …
- avec un verbe peu compatible avec *be* + V-*ing* : …

---

le présent en *be* + V-*ing*

Il est utilisé pour :
- décrire une action en cours de déroulement : …
- exprimer un point de vue dépréciatif : …
- annoncer la réalisation d'une action déjà envisagée : …

17 Traduisez.

1. Je ne fais pas la cuisine aujourd'hui.

2. Je pense déménager *(move)* à Londres.

3. Ce que je suis en train d'essayer de dire, c'est que tu ne peux pas revenir ici.

4. Si je ne fais pas ça maintenant, ce ne sera pas prêt ce soir.

5. Vous avez tous les deux besoin d'une coupure *(a break)*. Pourquoi ne partez-vous pas ?

6. J'ai pensé qu'il valait mieux que je te le dise : je pars. J'ai besoin de changement.

7. « Ta mère est d'accord ? – Oui. »

8. « C'est Patrick. Comment ça va ? – Patrick ! – J'espère que je ne vous dérange pas. »

9. « On s'occupera de lui, ne t'inquiète pas. – Tu veux me dire *(tell)* qu'il va mal ? »

10. Chaque soir, il raconte une histoire aux gosses et puis il va au lit.

Formes du prétérit simple §§ 48-50

18 Mettez le verbe entre parenthèses au prétérit simple. Attention aux verbes irréguliers (forme affirmative + ; forme négative – ; forme interrogative ?).

1. I (see +) your sister yesterday.
2. … you (fly ?) to New York?
3. She (teach +) English for two years.
4. She … (think –) about it.
5. I (think +) it would make you happy.
6. He (lose +) his key.
7. I (send +) the letter yesterday.
8. Why … you (send ?) it to the laundry?
9. He … (sleep –) well.
10. He (lay +) his briefcase on the table.
11. Why … you (lie ?)? You could have told the truth!
12. He (lie +) in bed, thinking of nothing.
13. He (fall +) downstairs.
14. She (feel +) very happy indeed.
15. He (bring +) me nice flowers.
16. How many … they (buy ?)?
17. It (mean +) she could not go.
18. She (lead +) them into the living room.

Emplois du prétérit simple §§ 51-56

19 Traduisez les phrases suivantes.

1. When I was eighteen I decided to study medicine.
2. "What should I say if I was asked when I last saw him?"
3. He talked to her as if she were a baby.
4. What would happen if I went?
5. She knocked off work early, said she had a headache, packed up and hit the road.
6. It would be best if you discussed this with her.
7. I'd much rather you didn't tell him.
8. If only I was their age and knew what I know now.

9. Sitting next to her, Adam shook his head. He was tall, dark. She thought he looked like one of those perfect men in magazine advertisements.

Prétérit simple ou prétérit en *be* + V-*ing* ? §60

20 Mettez le verbe entre parenthèses au prétérit simple ou au prétérit en *be* + V-*ing*.

1. I (think) while you are in the village you might have a word with Mr Blank.
2. Shortly before nightfall, a group of campers (enjoy) a barbecue near Ayers Rock. Suddenly, there (be) a shout.
3. Watches? Rings? Beck (not know) what she (talk) about and when she (persist) he (run) off to tell a policeman that a strange lady (annoy) him.
4. "What's going on here?" "That's precisely what I (ask)."
5. Something strange (happen) to me last night: I (go) home on foot and all the time I (have) the strange impression that someone (follow) me. I (turn) around several times but I never (see) anybody.
6. What you (do) when he (come) in?

21 Mettez le verbe entre parenthèses au prétérit simple ou au prétérit en *be* + V-*ing*.

Mr James S. (kill) his wife in a dream last night. He (dream) that his daughter who (sleep) in the same room (be attacked) by assassins and he (fire) on them, with the result that he (kill) his wife.

Yesterday Mr S., his wife and their two daughters (go) to bed as usual about 10. Towards midnight Mr S. (think) he (hear) the window open. Turning over, he (see) two masked men enter the room with knives. One (go) and (stand) over the daughter. In frantic terror Mr S. (fire) the pistol which he (clutch) in his hand beneath the pillow. Switching on the light he (see) that blood (trickle) from his wife's head. He then (realize) he had been dreaming but his wife (be) dead.

The Times, 27.11.1919.

Traduction de l'imparfait

22 Traduisez.

1. Elle avait 28 ans et elle allait conquérir le monde.
2. Elle ne savait pas ce qu'ils cherchaient.
3. Il demanda si elle savait à qui appartenaient les clefs.
4. Il ne voulait pas seulement lui plaire.
5. Les enfants n'écoutaient pas, ils étaient trop occupés à regarder le match.
6. Tous les soirs après le travail, il allait la voir chez elle ; il lui parlait de sa journée de travail ; elle faisait semblant *(pretend)* d'écouter.
7. C'était une belle matinée. Elle regarda autour d'elle : la rosée *(the dew)* brillait sur l'herbe, les oiseaux chantaient.
8. Lorsque les vagues déferlaient *(break)*, Jimmy était toujours à la plage. Il aimait faire du surf.

Formes du *present perfect*

§ 62

23 Mettez le verbe entre parenthèses au *present perfect* simple
(forme affirmative + ; forme négative − ; forme interrogative ?).

1. Where you (be ?)?
2. She (catch +) a mouse.
3. I (hear −) of him lately.
4. He (forget +).
5. They just (go +) out.
6. She (spend +) a lot of money.
7. you (speak ?) to him yet?
8. you (think ?) about it?
9. She (weep +) many tears.
10. We (pay −) the telephone bill yet.

24 Mettez le verbe entre parenthèses au *present perfect* en *be* +V-*ing*
(forme affirmative + ; forme négative − ; forme interrogative ?).

1. I (read +) .
2. you (smoke ?)?
3. They (fish +) for hours.
4. We (wait +) for hours.
5. How long they (look ?) for him?
6. What you (do ?)?
7. He (sleep +) for ten hours, it's time he woke up.
8. How long you (wear ?) glasses?
9. I (shop +) all day, my feet are dropping off.
10. I (ask +) you to mend the floor for six weeks.

For ou *since* ?

§ 66

25 Complétez les phrases suivantes avec *for* ou *since*, puis traduisez.

1. I've known him … eight years.
2. He travelled in Australia … six months.
3. It has been a long time … he played this sonata.
4. Have they actually been here … Monday?
5. I have not seen them … the birth of their son.
6. Can I leave this here … a few hours?

7. … when have you been watching TV?

8. She's been married … two years.

9. It's twenty years … she died.

10. I'll love him … ever.

26 Employez *for* ou *since* et mettez le verbe entre parenthèses au temps qui convient : *present perfect* simple ou en *be* + V-*ing*, *past perfect* simple ou en *be* + V-*ing*.

1. I (be stuck) at the same career grade … seven years.

2. He (be known) as Chubby … a teenager.

3. We want someone who has experience, who (do) this … a while.

4. It (rain) … ten days when I arrived in Edinburgh.

5. … 2000 our team (win) … the world championship five times.

6. The proportion of lone-parent families (triple) … 1991.

7. The woman (wander) round the car showroom … nearly an hour before a salesman at last offered to help.

8. Consider what (happen) to him … he turned twenty-five last August.

9. … July 1st large numbers of Californian teenagers (have) a hard time.

27 Traduisez.

1. Il est réveillé depuis trois heures. (*ou* Cela fait trois heures qu'il…)

2. Il est réveillé depuis trois heures de l'après-midi.

3. Il est en mer *(at sea)* depuis plus de six semaines.

4. Elle est professeur d'économie politique à Oxford depuis 2004.

5. Nous ne sommes pas payés depuis cinq semaines.

6. « Depuis combien de temps faites-vous cela ? – Depuis que j'ai quitté l'université, il y a neuf ans. »

7. Toute une année s'est écoulée depuis leur retour.

8. J'essaie d'ouvrir cette porte depuis 45 minutes.

9. Son roman est un best-seller depuis presque un an.

10. Le jardin était à l'abandon *(be neglected)* depuis des années quand nous l'avons acheté.

Present perfect simple ou en *be* + V-*ing* ? § 69-71

28 Traduisez.

1. Cela fait une éternité que tu téléphones. Tu n'as pas bientôt *(nearly)* fini ?
2. « Tu as l'air épuisée *(exhausted)*. – Oui, j'ai fait du jogging et cela fait des années que je n'ai pas couru. »
3. Qu'est-ce que tu fabriquais ? Ça fait des heures que je t'attends.
4. Tu as déjà fait ton travail *(homework)* ? Moi, je travaille depuis des heures et je n'ai pas encore fini.

29 Mettez le verbe entre parenthèses au temps qui convient.

1. He (sleep) since 10 o'clock; it's time he woke up!
2. He (sleep) through the alarm clock, that's why he's so late.
3. This is the most comfortable bed I (ever sleep) in.
4. I (teach) hundreds of students but I (never meet) such a hopeless group.
5. I (teach) for thirty years, so don't think you can teach an old dog new tricks!
6. "(smoke/you) today?" "Yes, four or five cigarettes."
7. The room smells. (smoke/you)?
8. He (paint) the ceiling, that's why the room looks so bright now.
9. "Her clothes are covered in paint." "Of course, she (paint)."
10. He (drink) two pints of beer. He shouldn't drive.

30 Mettez le verbe entre parenthèses au temps qui convient.

1. What happened to your hair? What (do/you) with yourself?
2. I (not laugh) so much in ages.
3. "I (try) to finish this exercise for hours. I wish you'd stop talking." "I (hardly say) anything."
4. "I (never see) you crying before." "It (not happen) for ages."
5. The peanut probably originated in Brazil although no fossils (be found) to prove this. But as long as people (make) pottery in South America, that is for about 3,500 years, they (make) jars decorated with peanuts. There was a lull *(une accalmie)* in the 60s but over the past three years the trade (grow) again.

Prétérit ou *past perfect* ?

31 Mettez le verbe entre parenthèses au prétérit ou au *past perfect*.

1. "Thank you very much," he said, astonished. He (never see) her so generous.
2. The next day she (move) away, as she (plan) to.
3. They wondered where she (go).
4. Sometimes they (talk) about places they (visit) together. They (never seem) to remember the same things.
5. When she (cry) for half an hour she (begin) to feel better.
6. For three weeks she (behave) as if nothing (change).
7. She thought perhaps he (forget).
8. When he came back, she (be) puzzled and a little hurt. (forget/he)?
9. She (take) the news as calmy as if she (expect) it.

32 Mettez le verbe donné entre parenthèses au prétérit ou au *past perfect*.

1. A Chicago judge today (grant) divorce to Mr R. on the grounds of his wife's silence. The plaintiff *(le plaignant)* (inform) the Court that, although his wife (live) in his house, she (not speak) to him for eighteen years. He (declare) that it (be) like living with a ghost. He (consult) physicians in the effort to get her to talk but it (be) impossible to surprise her into uttering a word.

The Times, 7.10.1922.

2. Through the arrest of three former prisoners of the San Quentin prison in California who (be released) on parole *(en liberté conditionnelle)* at various times last year, it (become) known today that counterfeit $ 10 bank notes, with which they (be supplied) (be manufactured) on the prison's own printing presses. In examining the men's prison records, the Secret Service (find) that all three (have) access to the printing shop while they were serving their terms.

The Times, 13. 2. 1936.

3. I (go) back to Oxford recently. I (not be) back since we all (leave), almost twenty years ago. I (be) surprised to see how little the city (change). Although there (be) new buildings everywhere and the main crossroads (be widened), the main landmarks (remain) in place.

Prétérit et *past perfect* simples ou en *be* + V-*ing* ?

33 Complétez avec le verbe entre parenthèses conjugué au temps qui convient : prétérit simple ou en *be* + V-*ing*, *past perfect* simple ou en *be* + V-*ing*.

1. It happened one Saturday morning: I (go) down to see if there (be) any post for me. I (pass) Wanda on the stairs. She (smile) with her letters in her hands. For me, there (be) a letter from my cousin. I (stand), beside the hall-stand, opening it.
Suddenly from Wanda's room (come) a long, loud cry.
2. He (stop) reading and (stare) at the wall across from his desk. The wall (need) painting. It (need) painting for years.
3. She (stand) in the doorway when he (begin) to speak: she (not have) time even to take off her coat.
4. On the third morning she (look) out of her bedroom window and (sniff) the air happily. It (be) a gentle grey morning with a smell of soft wet earth. The kind of smell that she (miss) for the past two years and a half. Wonderful to be home again, wonderful to be here in her own little bedroom which she (think) of so often when she (be) overseas.
5. Brian Blessed (cheat) death when his plane (crash-land) in a Venezuelan rain forest. The 61-year-old actor, who (film) The *Lost World* for BBC TV (have) to swim through a swamp *(un marécage)* for fear the plane would explode.

34 Complétez avec le verbe entre parenthèses conjugué au temps qui convient : prétérit simple ou en *be* + V-*ing*, *past perfect* simple ou en *be* + V-*ing*.

1. She (push) open the door. Women (sit) at the table. She (see) her mother among them. In five years her hair (go) grey and she (look) very old. Everyone (stop) what they (do).
2. "What (happen)?" "A massive heart attack. He (have) two or three warnings before but…" […] She (touch) her chest. "And he (have) these pains in the upper arm. I (tell) him to take his tablets. And off he (go) to open the bar. The next time I (see) him he (be) dead."

Bernard MacLaverty, Grace Notes.

Présent ou *present perfect* ?

35 Complétez les phrases en employant le verbe entre parenthèses au temps qui convient : présent simple ou en *be* + V-*ing*, *present perfect* simple ou en *be* + V-*ing*.

1. "I (go) out. (want/you) anything?"
2. "Pleased to meet you, Sandy. Where (come/you) from? " "I (come) from Maryville." "How long (be/you) here? " "I've just only arrived. "
3. (know/he) what we (talk) about?
4. What (plot/you four)?
5. The bus (leave) at half past ten.
6. "Your report is a disgrace." "It's not fair. I (try) hard, really."
7. He (run) this restaurant for more than twenty years.
8. It's the first time she (kiss) him.
9. "Wake up! It's the day I (wait) for. Come on, get up!" "What is it? I (sleep)!"
10. The jeans market (shrink). Jeans sales (slump) by more than three million pairs in the year to May. Yet, denim (remain) fashionable – as long as it's used for anything but jeans. Whether it (be) hip or nostalgic its appeal is universal.

36 Traduisez.

1. Que se passe-t-il lorsque les portes sont fermées ?
2. Qu'est-ce que c'est que tout ce bruit ? Que se passe-t-il ?
3. « Tu as entendu le téléphone ? – Oui, j'arrive. »
4. J'utilise ce stylo depuis des années.
5. Il a acheté son billet ce matin : il prend l'avion pour Londres cet après-midi.
6. C'est la première fois que je suis loin d'elle.
7. Tu dors tout le temps !
8. Cela fait combien de temps qu'il est assis là ?
9. C'est un problème qui nous menace *(creep up on)* depuis des années.
10. Tu as travaillé tout ce temps-là ?

37 Le passé composé : prétérit ou *present perfect* ? Traduisez.

1. Et la nuit dernière, tu as réussi à dormir ?
2. Tu n'as pas écouté ce qu'il a dit.
3. Nous y sommes allés il y a trois ans.

4. « Combien de comédies Shakespeare a-t-il écrites ? – Je ne sais pas, mais je les ai toutes lues. »

5. J'ai marché trop vite, c'est pourquoi je suis fatiguée.

6. Tu trembles. Tu as bu combien de cafés ?

7. Tu n'es pas revenu à la maison une seule fois en cinq ans.

8. « Pourquoi as-tu accepté ? – Je n'ai pas pu dire non. »

9. Qu'est-ce que tu as fait à ce couteau ? La lame *(the blade)* est tordue *(twisted)*.

10. « Nous allions commencer sans toi. – Désolée, je me suis perdue. »

38 Choisissez la forme verbale appropriée.

is working • works • has worked • worked • has been working • has never worked • does not work • did not work

1. Il **travaille** quarante heures par semaine.

2. Il **a** beaucoup **travaillé** la semaine dernière.

3. Elle est fatiguée, cela fait trois heures qu'elle **travaille**.

4. Elle **travaille** depuis cinq ans dans cette usine.

5. Tais-toi, il **travaille**.

6. Ça ne **marche** pas.

7. Ça ne **marchait** pas il y a deux semaines.

8. Ça n'**a** jamais **marché**.

wrote • has written • writes • has been writing

9. Il **a écrit** un article sur ce sujet.

10. Il y a quatre ans, il **a écrit** un article sur ce sujet.

11. Cela fait dix ans qu'il **écrit** pour *The Economist*.

12. Il **écrit** pour *The Economist*.

Prétérit ou *present perfect* ?

39 Relevez les verbes au prétérit, puis les verbes au *present perfect*. Soulignez les indices qui justifient l'emploi de l'un ou l'autre temps.

Carol Shields does not write about gangsters or spies. She once said: "I am interested in reality."

Gradually, this modest part-time academic, mother of five children, has become one of Canada's best-known novelists. She was born in Illinois in 1935, she attended the University of Ottawa and settled in Canada in 1957. She has lived there since that date.

"I guess I always wanted to be a writer," she says, "but it seemed impossible, like being a movie star."

She was awarded a Pulitzer Prize for *The Stone Diaries* which was published in 1993. *Larry's Party*, her latest novel, is likely to be widely successful. "I wanted to write about a man," she says, "I have written about men before but not, I think, very thoroughly or very well."

Carol Shields, in *Larry's Party*, has written a novel that examines a cultural revolution. "I think the biggest change of the millennium is the emergence of women as whole people. This is what feminism has always meant to me, just that women are wholly human. Before they were half beings. This change has had a tremendous impact on men – they have had to redefine what it means to be masculine."

Adapted from *The Good Book Guide*, October 1998. D.R.

40 Mettez le verbe entre parenthèses au prétérit ou au *present perfect*.

1. (taste/you) this new snack yet? It's delicious.

2. It wasn't the Americans who (invent) ice-cream. In 200 B.C. Chinese peasants (mix) snow with milk and rice and they (teach) the art of ice-cream making to the Indians. Ice-cream (become) now a part of the staple diet all over the world.

3. An eleven-year old boy (be electrocuted) at a sea-side amusement arcade. His body (be found) behind a machine. Police say that he (touch) the wires at the back of the machine and (be electrocuted).

4. It just (happen) when we (meet) at a club. We (swap: *échanger*) telephone numbers but I (not hear) from her since and she (not hear) from me.

5. Charleston, the city that (give) its name to a dance (step) into the limelight again.

6. The general tendency of industrialisation (be) to replace human skill by the skill of machines.

7. "Well, friends," the captain (say), "it seems we (make) it."

8. "Is your eyesight good?"

"I (never have) to wear spectacles."

"So, you have no doubt that the man you (see) that night is the prisoner?"

41 Mettez le verbe entre parenthèses au prétérit ou au *present perfect*.

1. Between 1914 and 1991 the world (change) more profoundly and more violently than at any time in history.
The history of the 20 years after 1973 is that of a world which (lose) its bearings and (slide) into instability and crisis.

2. "Bill Clinton says he (create) 11 million new jobs since he (become) president," a police officer in Annapolis, Maryland, (tell) me sarcastically in the autumn of 1996. "Sure he has. I have four of them."

Gavin ESLER, The United States of Anger.

3. The members of the scientific mission from Madrid (complete) their examination of the skeleton of the dinosaur discovered near Tetuan. They (come) to the conclusion that the remains are not those of a dinosaur at all. The mysterious "reptile" is a hay-making machine which (belong) to a Spanish farmer who (abandon) his property in 1917 during the Rifi war. The agricultural machinery (be enveloped) in a landslip caused by the heavy rains of that winter.

The Times, 30.1.1930.

Maîtriser les formes verbales

42 Complétez les phrases avec la forme verbale appropriée :
prétérit ou participe passé.

1. She (teach) English for two years and then decided to immigrate to Australia. There, she (meet) a surfer and (fall) in love with him.
2. When I was a kid I (read) a chapter of that book every night.
3. I have (know) him for years.
4. I (think) you had (forget) him.
5. He (lay) his attaché case on the desk and (leave).
6. I have never (ride) a camel.
7. She often (lie down) after lunch.
8. He (fall) downstairs and (break) his arm.
9. Have you (run) a business before?
10. He has (catch) a cold.

43 Complétez la traduction anglaise avec la forme verbale qui convient.

1. Combien d'argent a-t-il perdu ? *How much money did he …?*
2. As-tu compris ? *Have you …?*
3. Que vas-tu choisir ? *What are you going to …?*
4. Est-ce que la cloche a sonné ? *Has the bell …?*
5. Il m'a apporté des fleurs. *He has … me flowers.*
6. Il n'en a pas pensé grand-chose. *He … much of it.*
7. Il se mit aussitôt au travail. *He … to work at once.*
8. À quelle heure le soleil se lève-t-il ? *What time …?*
9. Est-ce que tu as retrouvé ton porte-monnaie ? *Have you … your wallet?*
10. Qui a écrit cette lettre ? *Who …?*

44 Conjuguez le verbe entre parenthèses au temps et à la forme indiqués (forme affirmative + ; forme négative – ; forme interrogative ?).

1. Every time someone (**tell +** : présent) me the world (**go +** : présent en *be* + V-*ing*) to end I simply (**believe –** : présent) it.
2. "What experience (**have ?** : *present perfect*) you and (**have ?** : present) you references?" "I (never **do +** : *present perfect*) anything quite like this before but I (**keep +** : *present perfect*) house for my mother for quite a time and I (**do +** : *present perfect*) quite a lot of cooking for dinner parties.
3. I wish you (**live –** : prétérit) in such a mess. And by the way where are all the books I (**bring +** : prétérit) you last time I (**come +** : prétérit)?
4. I wish everything (**become –** : prétérit en *be* + V-*ing*) so complicated.
5. We (**have +** : présent en *be* + V-*ing*) a wonderful time here. Why (you **come –** ? : présent) over and spend the weekend with us?

45 Conjuguez le verbe entre parenthèses au temps et à la forme indiqués (forme affirmative + ; forme négative – ; forme interrogative ?).

1. (you **know ?** : présent) what I (**say +** : *present perfect* en *be* + V-*ing*)? (you **understand ?** : présent)?
2. I (**tell +** : *present perfect*) you what you live for. You (**pay –** : prétérit en *be* + V-*ing*) attention. You live for the sake of living.
3. Miss M. was 82 when she (**die +** : prétérit).
4. I (**see +** : prétérit) at once he (**fight +** : *past perfect* en *be* + V-*ing*) for he had a black eye.
5. If I (**know +** : *past perfect*) I never would have gone.

6. People (**say +** : *present perfect* en *be* + V-i*ng*) for years that the Southwest is the new frontier in America. It certainly (**be +** : *present perfect*) true for me.

7. They (**pick up +** : prétérit) a hitchhiker. He (**carry +** : prétérit en *be* + V-i*ng*) a sack of tomatoes. They never (**see +** : *past perfect*) a man so happy to get a ride.

8. "It's time you (**turn +** : prétérit) out your light and (**go +** : prétérit) to sleep." "I (**finish –** : *present perfect*) my English yet." "What? I bet you (**work –** : *present perfect* en *be* + V-i*ng*). You (**read +** : *present perfect* en *be* + V-i*ng*) that Sears Roebuck catalogue. That's what you (**do +** : *present perfect* en *be* + V-i*ng*)"

9. If I (**stay +** : *past perfect* en *be* + V-i*ng*) for a long time, he wouldn't have been so friendly.

10. In 2007 they told him he (**go +** : prétérit en *be* + V-i*ng*) blind.

Formes du passif §78

46 Employez le verbe entre parenthèses à l'actif ou au passif, au temps demandé.

Présent

1. In the United States, most schools (start) at 8 every morning and classes (not finish) until 3 or 4 in the afternoon.
2. Many sports that in other countries (offer) by private clubs are available to American students at no cost.
3. Each year the SAT *(Scholastic Aptitude Test)* (take) by more than two million students.

Présent en *be* + V-*ing*

4. "Gifted children throughout Britain (neglect) by schools," the director of the National Association for gifted children recently declared. The association (press) the education minister to publish a report on the subject. It is also concerned that gifted children (overlook). Many parents of such children (opt) for private education.

Prétérit

5. This store (build) in 1899. It (remodel) in 1904 after it (partially destroy) by a fire. The north portion (acquire) in 1906. The first owner's son (operate) the business until 1977 when it (sell).
6. The greatest tragedy of the Gold Rush (occur) in 1898 when over 60 men (kill) in a snowslide. They (carry) back down the trail and (bury) near Dyea.

Present perfect

7. These researchers (spend) years studying children who are exceptionally gifted in mathematics.
8. This song (record) in almost every country on the planet.
9. English (largely replace) French as the language of diplomacy.
10. It (often say) that the best national anthems (write) by amateur musicians.
11. For many Burmese tribes life (not change) for centuries.

Modal + verbe à l'actif ou au passif

12. Means of purifying the air will (find) before life becomes unlivable.
13. Science will (come) up with a solution.
14. This may (easier say) than (do).

15. If you start at midday you may well (not close) the book until midnight.

16. For an extra £ 1 we will (send) your parcel by first class post. For an extra £ 10 your parcel will (send) "next day delivery" but orders must (place) by 1 p.m.

17. Our brochure will (give) more detailed information than can (include) here.

18. Can the suburbs (blame) for draining the life out of our cities?

19. How can we (make) our cities more civilised?

20. Children should (teach) to speak the truth.

47 Soulignez les formes passives, puis traduisez-les.

1. The concert was sponsored by the European Broadcasting Union and was being transmitted live to about twenty countries.

2. Things are simple or complex according to how much attention is paid to them.

3. For the past twenty years I have been a nurse manager of Ward 6 where children with chronic diseases are cared for. Three months ago I was asked to take over an additional ward.

4. Hotels and guesthouses are spread all over the island.

5. The baby must be in bed. And asleep. The washing must be done. And the dishes and God knows what.

6. This word is seldom used in contemporary English.

7. These nests (ces nids) are collected at great risk and are to be sold at £ 1,000 a kilogram for birds-nest soup.

8. There remain lots of things to be done.

9. She was born in 1990.

10. Children need to be played with and talked to.

Emplois du passif § 79-83

48 Transposez ces phrases au passif en prenant pour sujet l'élément en gras.

EXEMPLE : They have changed **the date**. ▷ The date has been changed.

1. Millions of viewers will watch **our programme**.

2. We must make **them** acceptable.

3. The Royal Ocean Racing Club instituted **the Admiral's Cup** in 1957.

4. He rarely punished anyone but everyone obeyed **him**.

5. The last time the Cutty Sark carried tea from China was in 1877 and by then the steamers were bringing back **most of the tea**.
6. His father had told **him** about them.
7. The president will greet **those who arrive first**.
8. Scientists at the University of Ottawa have carried out **several experiments in that field**.
9. In the modern world technology has replaced **magic**.
10. Who wrote **it**?

49 Transposez ces phrases au passif lorsque c'est souhaitable pour mettre l'objet de l'action en valeur.

1. People tell me there will be a delay of six weeks.
2. A visitor will bring you good news.
3. They will open the park gates at 5 a.m. They usually lock them at night.
4. The inhabitants of the village gave money and young people offered to work.
5. Thieves were regularly stealing goods from his shop. So he set a trap.
6. The ball hit the batsman on the leg, on his trouser pocket.
7. They had announced the news of the strike on April 30th.
8. A group of nature lovers are trying to persuade the paint manufacturers not to continue making paint which contains insecticide.
9. If people painted every house with insecticide paint, it would seriously disturb the balance of nature.

50 Répondez aux énoncés en employant une forme active ou passive du verbe entre parenthèses, conjugué au temps qui convient.

EXEMPLE : "Why didn't she come?" "She (not invite)" ▷ "She was not invited."

1. "Why couldn't she get into the pub?" "People under 16 (not admit)."
2. "Is this house very old?" "Yes, it (build) in 1880."
3. "Why are you so late?" "The plane (delay)."
4. "Is he a dangerous maniac?" "Yes, he ought to (lock up)."
5. "Why is he so optimistic?" "He is sure he can (solve the problem)."
6. "He should be sentenced for life, right?" "I (not agree)."
7. "Why is she so upset?" "She (not offer the job)."
8. "Why is he so happy?" "His colleagues (give) him a TV set when he retired."

9. "Do you know William Turner?" "Yes, he was an English painter who (recognize) as a revolutionary genius, (make) his name with painting seascapes and (leave) some three hundred paintings."

51 Transformez ces phrases suivant le modèle.

EXEMPLE : It is said that he drinks champagne at breakfast.
▷ He is said to drink champagne at breakfast.

1. It is acknowledged that education is the prime purpose of maintaining the national museums.
2. It is considered that Frank Lloyd Wright was the greatest American architect of the 20th century.
3. It is known that Chicago is the birthplace of the first skyscrapers.
4. It is understood that the man, who will be questioned by police today, has been a member of the Gun Club for the last five years.
5. It was reported later that he was dismayed at the circumstances in which he was interviewed.
6. It is believed that she paid £ 350 to get a ticket.
7. It is believed that the couple suffered domestic problems recently.
8. It is expected that this gold nugget will fetch around £ 200,000 at auction.

52 Complétez ces phrases en utilisant les verbes proposés à la forme et au temps voulus.

put an end to • lose sight of • guess at • discriminate against • look into • disapprove of • look after • refer to • apply for • shout down

1. In some countries ethnic minorities … still …
2. Those children are untidy. They … not properly …
3. A visa has to … six months before departure.
4. Yesterday at the meeting he … by the crowd.
5. They have signed an agreement: at long last *(enfin)* the conflict …
6. "What of his complaint?" "It … but it's likely to last for a while."
7. She … two years ago and nobody has heard of her ever since.
8. Western-style values and culture … by the New Age Movement.
9. There were 40 people employed but details of the construction can only …
10. The two towers of the Marina City in Chicago are often … as the "Corn Cobs".

Le renvoi à l'avenir §84-90

53 Choisissez l'expression appropriée pour compléter ces phrases.

1. There's something ominous about being 65 years old. Suddenly, old age is not a phenomenon which … ; it has occurred.
• is occurring • will occur • is going to occur

2. "The day …," he prophesied, "when you … you aren't as smart as you think you are."
• will come – are going to find out • is going to come – find out
• is going to come – will find out

3. "So, we're all going now, and what about Uncle Jim? … he … too?" she asked.
• is he going to come • is he about to come • is he coming

4. "No, he … at the farm."
• will stay • is staying • is going to stay

5. "He … the place going."
• 'll keep • is keeping • is going to keep

6. I … you before Thursday but if you can't make it, can you call me up?
• 'll probably see • am probably going to see • am probably seeing

7. I … anything you …
• am going to sell – are buying • 'll sell – will buy • will sell – are going to buy

8. I'm warning you. You … out of a job if you don't wake up!
• will be • are • are going to be

54 Traduisez.

1. Nous saurons ce soir.
2. Il part dans quelques jours.
3. C'est facile, je vais te montrer.
4. « Qu'est-ce que vous voulez boire ? – Je prendrai du thé. »
5. J'y croirai lorsque je le verrai.
6. « Est-ce que tu peux venir dimanche ? – Désolée, je ne peux pas, je vais au théâtre. »
7. Il n'a pas l'intention de prendre sa retraite (retire) maintenant, il a trop à faire.

8. Bon, je vais vous dire ce que nous allons faire.

9. Le spectacle va commencer.

10. Je ne vais pas regarder le match, j'ai du travail.

55 Complétez les phrases en employant *will* + V, *will have* + participe passé ou *will be* + V-*ing*.

1. By the end of the month around 800,000 people (see) the sensational exhibition.

2. "Having this exhibition at Gatwick Airport is fantastic because it (reach) all sorts of people," the organizer said.

3. This was one of the most popular programmes on television. "They (discuss) this story line in every pub, office, and factory in Britain tomorrow," he said.

4. I wanted to know. When (move out/you)?

5. Shopping with Eurostar is so easy that you (want) to repeat the experience, we can guarantee it.

6. It made me think how lovely it would be if you could preserve your memories in a book so that you (leave) your mark in the world.

7. I could give you some money for the time and trouble you (spend) on our project.

8. With our new facial cream your complexion (look) smoother in one day, seem younger in just one week.

9. In the time it takes you to read this paragraph another three vulnerable youngsters (lose) their lives.

Le conditionnel

§ 96-100

56 Complétez ces phrases en mettant le verbe entre parenthèses à la forme appropriée du conditionnel.

1. What (do/you) if I left you?

2. If I were you, I (not worry) about the future.

3. What (tell/he) her if she had asked?

4. They (be) glad if you could come.

5. Supposing it rained that (not be) much fun.

6. If she had followed his advice she (may succeed).

7. I'm thirsty: I (can do) with a cup of tea.

8. It's up to you but I (not accept) his invitation.

9. I (imagine) you were glad to hear from him.

10. She thought she (cannot live) without him.

Degrés de certitude

§ 106-109

57 Soulignez les modaux puis classez les phrases du plus certain au moins certain. Traduisez.

1. It might be a good idea.
2. There must have been someone beside them to drive the car.
3. I thought you might like to see the children before they went to bed.
4. She may have been responsible for the accident.
5. He could very well win a thousand dollars.
6. The phone rang. "That'll be for me," he said.
7. He might become famous one day.
8. There must be better songs to sing than this.
9. He can't be dead!
10. She should be back in a few minutes.
11. It couldn't happen again.

- très certain : …
- très probable : …
- possible : …
- incertain : …
- imaginable : …
- difficilement imaginable : …
- impossible : …

---

58 Reformulez les phrases suivantes en employant un modal.

1. a) You are certainly joking.
   b) I am sure he was lying.
2. a) I think you will be surprised.
   b) Maybe he gave her a diamond ring.
3. a) Perhaps we'll never see each other again.
   b) I don't know where she is. Perhaps she is waiting for us at the airport.
4. a) I am sure she is not as old as you say she is.
   b) I am sure she's not sleeping, not at this time of day!
   c) I am sure I have not lost his address.
5. a) I suppose he speaks English fluently: he has lived in London for three years.
   b) They are almost certain to have arrived now.

59 Traduisez.

1. Il se pourrait qu'elle devienne vétérinaire *(a vet)*.
2. Il doit y avoir une autre solution.
3. « Tu penses qu'il pourrait être absent *(be gone)* un mois ?
– Ça se pourrait. »
4. Il se peut qu'elle n'aime pas cette idée.
5. Il doit avoir trois ou quatre ans de moins qu'elle.
6. Ça a dû se passer juste avant la guerre.
7. Ça pourrait être très embarrassant *(embarrassing)* si on nous voyait ensemble.
8. On aurait pu croire qu'il était ivre.
9. Pourquoi as-tu jeté ces vêtements ? Quelqu'un aurait pu en vouloir.

Capacité, propriété du sujet   § 110-113

60 Complétez les phrases en utilisant *can/can't*, *could/couldn't*, *will* ou *would*, puis traduisez-les.

1. I wish I … stay here for ever.
2. I can explain if you … only listen.
3. Interflora has launched a website so that you … send flowers from work without even picking up the phone.
4. This classic white shirt … stand the test of time.
5. You … buy anything here, from oysters to cigars!
6. Bears are mostly vegetarian, but they … eat whatever meat they … catch or find.
7. What I … stand is the thought of him lying and lying for all those years.
8. … you do me a favour?
9. James Dean was her hero at that time. She … save every photograph from the magazines and she fixed them to the walls of her bedroom.
10. Come with me, … you?

61 Complétez les phrases en utilisant *can/can't*, *could/couldn't*, *will* ou *would*, puis traduisez-les.

1. "I … remember the address." "… you even remember the street?"
2. "He says you're foolish to take such a risk." "He …! He's always finding fault with me!"

3. When I was a child I … understand adults, and now that I am an adult I … understand children.

4. They … have us believe that the situation is improving but the plain fact is that it's getting worse.

5. … you be so kind as to lend me your laptop?

6. He said it was perfectly obvious, as far as he … see.

7. If only he … have spent the night here!

8. When the car started he said, "Wonders … never cease!"

9. I had an alarm clock which was set for nine o'clock, but invariably every morning I … wake up before then.

10. I had not heard from them for as long as I … remember but I knew they were still alive.

62 Modal + V ou modal + *have* + participe passé ? Traduisez.

1. Je ne pourrais pas le quitter. Où irais-je ?

2. Je n'aurais pas pu le quitter. Où serais-je allée ?

3. Tu devrais lui parler parce que tu peux répondre à ses questions.

4. Tu aurais dû lui parler parce que tu aurais pu répondre à ses questions.

5. Elle préférerait que tu écrives en anglais.

6. Elle aurait préféré que tu écrives en anglais.

7. Certainement les choses pouvaient s'améliorer, la vie pouvait être meilleure.

8. Certainement les choses auraient pu s'améliorer, la vie aurait pu être meilleure.

9. Tu n'aurais rien à perdre et tu pourrais avoir beaucoup à y gagner.

10. Tu n'aurais rien eu à perdre et tu aurais peut-être eu beaucoup à y gagner.

63 Modal + V ou modal + *be* + V-*ing* ? Complétez les phrases avec la forme appropriée du verbe entre parenthèses.

1. Rome wasn't built in a day. You must (take) time.

2. "Where is she?" "I think she's upstairs. She must (read)."

3. He wondered what he was doing here when he should (ride) far away from San Francisco.

4. What about a glass of champagne? I really think we should (celebrate).

5. You can always (tell) a person by their shopping.

6. They can't (have) lunch at this time of day!

7. "I wonder where she is." "She could (play) tennis."

8. I couldn't (hear) what they were saying.

9. She doesn't want to be disturbed: she might (work) at the moment.

10. Might I (suggest) a nice dry white wine?

64 Infinitif, be + V-*ing* ou *have* + participe passé du verbe ?
Employez le verbe entre parenthèses à la forme qui convient.

1. "Mr Parkins?" I asked. "The same," he said. "And you must (be) Mr Banks. I'm honoured to meet you, sir."

2. "You say they stopped you at the frontier. That must (be) rather frightening." "So it was."

3. "Can I do anything?" "Yes, we're running out of glasses already. Everyone must (leave) them around." "I'll go round and see what I can find and wash some."

4. "Shall we go back?" "Go back?" "Yes, something may (go) wrong if we don't."

5. If she had only had half your beauty and character, I might (love) her.

6. If you're going to be in town we might (have) coffee together.

65 Infinitif, *be* + V-*ing* ou *have* + participe passé du verbe ?
Employez le verbe entre parenthèses à la forme qui convient.

1. "Where did you go?" "I posted that letter to Hans." "Couldn't it (wait) until the morning?"

2. "What do you think of him as a student?" "I had to give him a B. He could (do) better but he got rattled *(il a paniqué)*."

3. These women are paid so little that they can't possibly (do) it for the money.

4. I'm afraid I can't (explain) it to you now.

5. I searched for my wallet but I couldn't (find) it. Could I (drop) it on the train?

6. "You knew I was here? You should (call) me."

7. "I'd like to see your house." "You should (come) to dinner."

8. I shouldn't (come). What would my mother say if she knew?

Volonté du sujet

§ 114-115

66 Traduisez les phrases suivantes en faisant appel à *will* ou *would*.

1. Qui veut venir avec nous ?
2. Vous voudriez bien me rendre un service ?
3. Vous voulez bien me rappeler plus tard ?
4. J'aimerais *(I wish)* que ça marche.
5. Je pense qu'elle refusera de répondre à cette question.
6. J'aimerais *(I wish)* que quelqu'un réponde.
7. Elle refuse d'y aller, un point c'est tout.
8. Tu veux bien fermer la porte, s'il te plaît ?
9. Elle aimerait *(She wishes)* qu'il ne se plaigne pas tout le temps.
10. Elle refusait de le laisser payer.

Obligation et conseil ; autorisation

§ 116-117 ; 118-119

67 Soulignez les modaux et classez-les selon les valeurs données ci-dessous. Traduisez les phrases.

> - contraindre, donner un ordre : …
> - interdire : …
> - offrir, suggérer de : …
> - donner un conseil : …
>
> - accorder une permission : …
> - demander une permission : …
> - refuser une permission : …

Emplois fréquents
1. Left lane must turn left.
2. Can I leave my stuff here?
3. Could I speak to you, Sir?
4. I think you should see a doctor.
5. He shouldn't have talked to you about that.
6. May I remind you that all this is being done for your benefit?
7. Shall I take that plate?
8. You must not tell lies.
9. If you're under 17, you can't drive a car in Britain.
10. You can both go. I don't need you.

Emplois moins fréquents
11. Thou shalt not steal.
12. Might I speak to you for a moment?
13. Each voter may vote for one candidate.
14. Two parallel white lines mean that you may not overtake.
15. You might have a word with him on that subject.

68 Traduisez.
1. J'ai faim. Je peux avoir quelque chose à manger *(have a snack)* ?
2. Vous devez obéir à la loi.
3. Tu peux m'emprunter mon journal si tu veux.
4. Puis-je voir votre passeport, s'il vous plaît ?
5. Désirez-vous que je vous aide ?
6. Tu n'aurais pas dû boire autant.
7. Ils devraient être au lit, pas en train de regarder la télévision.
8. Il est interdit de nourrir les animaux. *(Visitors ...)*
9. Pourrais-je vous donner un conseil ?
10. Est-ce que je pourrais me servir de votre téléphone ?
11. Il fallait me le dire !
12. Il ne faut pas y toucher.

Emplois non conditionnels de *should* § 120-124

69 Traduisez.
1. Il est étrange qu'il ne soit pas là.
2. Au cas où il demanderait, dis-lui que je reviendrai mercredi.
3. Que suggérez-vous que je prenne ?
4. C'est drôle que tu dises ça.
5. Il est important que vous écoutiez attentivement.
6. Ils ont insisté pour que nous dinions avec eux.
7. Si jamais vous changez d'avis, faites-le-moi savoir.
8. Il est absurde qu'elle soit payée moins que lui.
9. Je lui ai donné une carte de peur qu'elle ne se perde.
10. Il a suggéré qu'elle vende sa voiture.

Should ou *would* ?

§ 95, 96, 116, 120-124, 444

70 *Should* ou *would* ? Complétez les phrases suivantes.

1. I dread to think what your poor father … have thought.
2. "Don't you get bored?" "Why … I get bored?"
3. "What … you like first? The good news or the bad news?"
4. "Maybe I … change my name?" "What … you change it to?"
5. I called the police right away. They … be here by now.
6. I don't know why this … have happened to me.
7. If only things … stop happening, but they never do, don't you agree?
8. "How long until supper?" "About half an hour. Your father … be home by then."
9. "Shall we meet at five, at the library?" "That … be fine."
10. It wasn't my fault if I was late. The car … n't start.

71 Traduisez les phrases suivantes.

1. What **should** I say? How am I going to put it?
2. My life was over and things **would** never be the same again.
3. When I asked her why she married Bob she **would** say she had no choice.
4. She used to say we **should** make the most of what we had.
5. There were five bedrooms, and it was only natural that Charlie **should** have the biggest.
6. She could do something better. I wish you **would** talk to her about going to university.
7. I suppose I thought it **would** always go on like that.
8. "Do you think this is the place?" "Yes, it **should** be just here."
9. **Would** you help me with this?
10. She was a very patient cat. She **would** sit for hours, bird watching.

72 Complétez les phrases en employant *can, can't* ou *be (un)able to*
à la forme qui convient.

1. I carry more secrets than you … imagine.
2. For the first two years I saved so that we … buy the house of our dreams.
3. Neither of them asked me why. If they had I … have answered.
4. Do you think you'll … fix it?
5. He told her she … keep the letter if she wanted to.
6. Now you … see why I am worried.
7. Have you ever dreamt that you … make an emergency phone call?
8. He seemed to know whom he … pick on (*harceler*) and whom he …
9. Yesterday I … drive 500 miles although the weather was terrible.
10. Her first name was India. She … never … get used to it.

73 Complétez ces phrases en employant *would, used to* ou *be used to*
à la forme qui convient.

1. When she wanted something she … just have to ask and I … see if we could afford it.
2. He … be President of the Rotary Club in Winchester.
3. She no longer worried: she … now … waking suddenly in the night, sometimes from alarming dreams, sometimes from nothing.
4. He … throw a tantrum *(piquer une crise)* if his cup of tea wasn't waiting for him at 10.
5. This is exactly how I … feel when you were little.
6. "Do you know them?" "Yes they're friends of my parents'. I … play with their son in the paddling pool."
7. He doesn't feel lonely: he … spending hours alone, watching the sea, writing poetry.
8. There … be an important fruit and vegetable market in Covent Garden.

74 *Ought to, had better* ou *should* ? Traduisez.

1. Il ferait mieux de ne pas conduire.
2. Tu ne devrais pas prêter attention *(take any notice of)* à ce qu'il te dit.
3. Je crois qu'il vaudrait mieux que je parte. J'ai besoin d'être seul *(be on my own)*.

4. « Il devrait dormir maintenant. – Vous pensez qu'il va s'en sortir
(be alright) ? – Il est seulement choqué *(be in a shock)*. Quelques heures
de repos devraient tout arranger *(take care of it)*. »

5. J'ai décidé qu'il valait mieux que je sois présent lorsqu'elle le
rencontrerait.

6. J'ai encore la grippe. Je devrais être au lit à la maison.

7. Il vaudrait mieux que tu réfléchisses bien à ce que tu vas faire.

8. C'est un scandale *(a disgrace)*. Il devrait y avoir une pancarte
(a notice).

9. C'était une enfant. Elle n'aurait pas dû connaître ce genre de chose.

10. J'aurais dû prendre un taxi au lieu de rentrer à pied.

75 Complétez avec *must, must not, have to* ou *don't have to*.

1. She will be hard to deal with, even to speak to at first. He … be
prepared for this.

2. Turn the radio down, please, so you can hear what I … say.

3. She … cry again, it will only exhaust her and besides, it's useless.

4. These arguments … convince her, since they are true.

5. "I'll drive you home." "You … do that. I can walk."

6. I can't go but it … let it stop you if that's really what you want.

7. I just … do what I can with what I am, which is what everyone … do.

8. Anyway, you … admit that it was pretty funny.

9. You'll … wait here until we get this checked by a doctor.

10. "How was your vacation?" "Oh, disappointing." "Oh? You … tell me
about it."

76 Complétez avec *must, must not, have to* ou *don't have to*.

1. She glanced at the clock. "You … go," she stated, "right away."

2. You … absolutely go to bed, with a fever like that.

3. If you didn't go to that concert, I wish you'd tell me. You … lie to me.

4. "Have you anything planned today?" "I … go to university this
morning."

5. Jane? Well, you … admit she's in a difficult position.

6. You … go on with it if you don't want to.

7. The race isn't won yet, I know I … concentrate but I … get too tense.

8. He runs to work. He … worry about traffic jams.

77 Employez *need* à la forme qui convient.

1. You … not drive so fast: we have plenty of time.
2. She is well again: she … to take more pills.
3. They … not worry: they will succeed.
4. You … not write to her: she will be here tomorrow.
5. There's plenty of food in the fridge: I … to go shopping.

78 Traduisez en employant *need*.

1. Tu n'avais pas besoin de conduire vite : nous avions tout notre temps.
2. Elle allait bien : il n'était pas nécessaire qu'elle continue à prendre des pilules.
3. Ce n'était pas la peine qu'ils s'inquiètent : ils réussiraient.
4. Tu n'avais pas besoin de lui écrire.
5. Il y avait largement assez de provisions dans le frigo : je n'avais pas besoin d'aller faire des courses.

79 Les équivalents de « devoir ». Traduisez ces phrases.

1. Je dois dire que j'ai été plutôt surprise.
2. Il ne voit pas très bien : il doit porter des lunettes.
3. Tu devras t'y habituer.
4. Pourquoi doivent-ils lui obéir ?
5. Il devait mourir quatre ans plus tard.
6. Il a dû manquer son train.
7. Tu dois faire comme on te dit.
8. Ils doivent se marier dans deux mois.
9. Tu dois avoir hâte de le revoir.
10. Il devait être en Angleterre lorsque l'accident s'est produit.

80 Traduisez en complétant les éléments indiqués.

1. C'est drôle que tu dises ça.
It is funny that …
2. Elle a insisté pour que je reste.
She insisted that …
3. Il a suggéré que nous nous arrêtions.
He suggested that …
4. Si tel est le cas, il partira.
If … he will go.
5. Quoi qu'il advienne, il ne changera pas d'avis.
… he will not change his mind.
6. Si j'étais à votre place, je prendrais rendez-vous.
If … I would make an appointment.
7. À tes souhaits !
(God) …
8. Il est essentiel qu'il soit préparé à ça.
It is essential that …
9. Si besoin est, je peux faire une photocopie.
If … I can photocopy it.
10. Son excuse, pour ainsi dire, ressemblait à une insulte.
His apology, …, sounded like an insult.

81 Traduisez.

1. Reviens !
2. Demandons-lui !
3. Ne cours pas !
4. Sois sage !
5. Je t'en prie, fais attention !
6. Ne nous plaignons pas.
7. Fais ce qu'on te dit.
8. Qu'ils ne s'en aillent pas !
9. Laisse-le tranquille.
10. Tu veux bien écouter ?

13 | Les reprises elliptiques

82 Traduisez les réponses ou les questions brèves.

1. "Has he changed?" « *Oh, oui !* »
2. "Did you know her?" « *Non.* »
3. "She loves him." « *Oui.* »
4. "So, you won't come." « *Mais si !* »
5. "Who spoke first?" « *Simon.* »
6. "They have found it." « *Ah, oui ?* »
7. "Are you kidding?" « *Non.* »
8. "He lives in Ireland." « *Ah, oui ?* »
9. "Is it open to the public?" « *Je ne pense pas.* »
10. "Will you join us?" « *J'aimerais beaucoup.* »

83 Traduisez les réponses ou les questions brèves.

1. "Can I go too?" « *Tu n'as pas le droit.* »
2. "He has forgotten her." « *J'ai bien peur que oui.* »
3. "She caught the train in time." « *Oui, je pense.* »
4. "She can manage alone. " « *Bien sûr que oui.* »
5. "Has he telephoned yet?" « *J'ai bien peur que non.* »
6. "She rang about an hour ago." « *Ah, oui ?* »
7. "Why are you standing here?" « *Parce qu'on nous l'a dit.* »
8. "You ought to tell him." « *Je ne sais pas comment.* »

84 Traduisez les réponses en anglais en employant *so, neither* ou la négation simple.

1. "She plays the violin beautifully." « *Lui aussi.* »
2. "He knew all about it. " « *Eux non.* »
3. "I entirely agree with him." « *Moi pas.* »
4. "It looks like rain." « *C'est vrai.* »
5. "I've never felt so exhausted." « *Moi non plus.* »
6. "Peter is not here today." « *Effectivement.* »
7. "I'll be at the meeting." « *Moi aussi.* »
8. "I've no idea where we are going." « *Moi non plus.* »
9. "He didn't remember the trip was cancelled." « *Moi non plus.* »
10. "She'd love to go to Canada." « *Lui aussi.* »

85 Complétez les phrases par un *question tag*.

1. She is twelve, …?
2. They aren't tired, …?
3. You spoke to me, …?
4. They won't like it, …?
5. Everybody laughed, …?
6. You seldom see her, …?
7. None could do it, …?
8. Let's go, …?
9. There was a lot of noise, …?
10. You will come, …?

Le groupe nominal

Le genre du nom § 163-164

86 Donnez le féminin des noms suivants.

man • father • uncle • nephew • husband • lion • bull • fox • dog • boy-friend • male • bear • actor • waiter • tom-cat • god • barman • horse • son-in-law • pig

87 Chassez l'intrus.

1. nurse • man • bear • he-goat
2. waitress • she-bear • actress • lioness
3. ship • actor • lion • boy
4. chairperson • friend • spokesman • baby
5. aunt • niece • teacher • sister

Le nombre du nom § 165-174

88 Classez les noms suivants en trois groupes,
en fonction de la prononciation de leur pluriel : [z], [s] ou [ɪz].

self • idea • wish • group • peach • office • kid • member • church • book • tomato • ear • neck • chief • corporation • bachelor • unit • system

89 Relevez les noms pluriels de ce texte et classez-les
en fonction de leur prononciation : [z], [s] ou [ɪz].

Invasion of the snails

They came out of their shells, they saw, and they're conquering the gardens of Britain. Snails — in numbers never witnessed before — are on the march, making a meal of the nation's herbaceous borders and turning the lawns and paths into crunchy obstacle courses.

The sheer size of the invasion has prompted unprecedented demand for pest pellets from gardeners who fear for their bedding plants, flowers — roses, carnations, dahlias — vegetables and fruit — tomatoes, salads, carrots, strawberries. Although snails are the most noticeable pests in the garden, slugs are a far bigger problem.

Adapted from *Daily Mail*, 7.7.1998.

90 Mettez au pluriel les noms suivants (assurez-vous de leur sens).

brush • chief • crossroads • photo • path • species • ghetto • criterion • thief • crisis • loaf • brother • potato • medium • leaf • analysis • wolf • phenomenon • aircraft

91 Mettez au pluriel les noms suivants.

man • child • louse • foot • ox • mouse • tooth • goose • thesis • campus

92 Mettez au pluriel les noms suivants, quand cela est possible. Justifiez vos choix.

EXEMPLES : *story* ▷ *stories* (consonne + *y* ▷ consonne + *ies* au pluriel ; nom dénombrable) ; *cash* ▷ pas de pluriel (nom indénombrable)

grass • leaf • staff • illness • youth • dish • box • porch • robbery • business • kingdom • silence

93 Chassez l'intrus.

1. tomato • hero • potato • photo
2. lady • anxiety • boy • baby
3. leaf • cliff • calf • shelf
4. book • foot • tooth • goose
5. fish • trout • salmon • plaice
6. aircraft • deer • sheep • mouse
7. army • cast • crowd • people
8. cattle • rubbish • management • vermin
9. news • means • species • barracks

94 Associez les noms indénombrables suivants aux expressions utilisées pour désigner un élément de ce qu'ils représentent.

EXEMPLE : scissors – a pair of ▷ a pair of scissors

noms indénombrables
grass • compasses • luck • cattle • toast • lightning • thunder • jeans • sugar • snow

expressions utilisées pour désigner un élément
a slice of • a blade of • a pair of • a stroke of • a flake of • a lump of • a head of • a flash of • a crash of

95 Expliquez la différence de sens entre :

1. two pennies *et* two pence
2. fruits *et* fruit
3. darts are... *et* darts is...
4. draughts are... *et* draughts is...
5. the customs are... *et* the customs is...
6. two compasses *et* two pairs of compasses

96 Tous les noms ci-dessous comportent un *-s* final. Classez-les en trois catégories : ceux qui sont suivis d'un verbe au singulier, ceux qui sont suivis d'un verbe au pluriel, ceux qui acceptent les deux accords.

glasses • athletics • savings • politics • barracks • clothes • headquarters • outskirts • news • shorts • spectacles • remains

97 Choisissez le verbe qui convient.

1. A number of people (has/have) complained about the noise made by aircraft taking off.
2. I think ten pounds (is/are) too much to pay for such a little thing.
3. She picked up her belongings, which (was/were) lying on the floor, and left.
4. The deer that (lives/live) in my forest (is/are) dear to me.
5. The hotel staff (does/do) not like the new manager's wife.
6. More than one house (has/have) been broken into during the holidays.
7. The police (think/thinks) that one of the witnesses (is/are) lying.
8. Bacon and eggs (is/are) what the English often (has/have) for breakfast.

98 Mettez le verbe entre parenthèses à la forme voulue.

1. Mathematics (have) always been my favourite subject.
2. The salmon (swim) up this river to lay eggs.
3. Look! The cattle (be) grazing in the meadow.
4. My family (gather) at Christmas every year.
5. The crew (be) now waiting for instructions from the captain.
6. Yesterday, police (be) rushed to the scene of the accident.
7. This news (be) alarming.

99 Tous ces noms de pays finissent par un -s. Classez-les en deux catégories : ceux qui sont suivis d'un verbe au singulier, ceux qui sont suivis d'un verbe au pluriel.

the Bahamas • Cyprus • Honduras • the Netherlands • the Philippines • the Maldives • Wales • the United States of America • the West Indies

Dites ce qui caractérise ceux qui admettent un verbe au pluriel.

100 Mettez les noms composés suivants au pluriel (vérifiez leur sens).

a son-in-law • a goods-train • a manservant • a tooth-brush • a woman-hater • a passer-by • a grown-up • a sit-in • a step-father

101 Traduisez.

1. Essaie de ne pas oublier tes bagages à l'aéroport !
2. Tu devrais suivre mes conseils.
3. Je ne trouve pas mon pantalon.
4. J'ai acheté de nouveaux meubles pour mon appartement.
5. Kicking John a été le meilleur gardien de but de la coupe du monde.

102 Traduisez.

1. Le quartier général des partis politiques est protégé par la police.
2. Le public n'a pas encore été informé des dernières nouvelles.
3. La caserne a été détruite par l'armée.
4. Les spectateurs étaient si contents qu'ils ont applaudi les acteurs au milieu de la pièce.
5. Dix policiers ont été blessés dans les émeutes.
6. Tous les bagages sont examinés à la douane.
7. Les membres de ma famille sont blonds aux yeux bleus.
8. Le gouvernement américain a décidé d'amplifier sa lutte contre le terrorisme.
9. Je n'ai pas trouvé de meilleur moyen de le faire.
10. Deux avions se sont écrasés après le décollage *(take-off)*.

L'article Ø

§ 175-181

103 Traduisez.

1. L'homme et la femme sont censés être égaux.
2. Le courage, l'amour, la générosité sont des valeurs rares.
3. La vitesse peut tuer, la drogue aussi.
4. Si vous mettez trop d'huile dans la poêle *(saucepan)*, elle risque de prendre feu.
5. Je devrai y aller en voiture ou en avion, vu que les conducteurs de train *(train drivers)* sont en grève *(be on strike)*.

104 Traduisez.

1. L'hôpital est entre l'école et l'église : je me souviens être allée à l'école et à l'église ici, mais pas à l'hôpital.
2. J'aime les livres, même si je ne les lis pas.
3. Qu'as-tu mangé au petit-déjeuner ?
4. Le bleu et l'orange sont mes couleurs préférées.
5. Tout le monde devrait parler l'anglais de nos jours *(nowadays)*.

105 Traduisez.

1. Des maladies comme le cancer, le SIDA, l'hépatite *(hepatitis)* seront peut-être un jour de mauvais souvenirs.
2. Les jours sont beaucoup plus courts en hiver qu'au printemps.
3. J'ai dû rester quinze jours au lit à cause d'un mauvais rhume.
4. J'ai en assez de la télévision.
5. Je ne connais personne vivant en Amérique du Nord ou en Australie.

106 Classez ces groupes nominaux en français selon qu'ils expriment une généralité ou quelque chose de spécifique.

1. Les miroirs sont des glaces qui ne fondent pas.

Paul MORAND

2. Le style est une façon très simple de dire des choses compliquées.

3. La lune est le soleil des statues.

4. L'enfance sait ce qu'elle veut. Elle veut sortir de l'enfance.

Jean COCTEAU

> Valeur de généralité : …
> Valeur spécifique : …

107 Traduisez les groupes nominaux français que vous venez de classer.

108 Donnez l'équivalent en français des proverbes suivants.

1. Speech is silver, but silence is golden.
2. Appetite comes with eating.
3. Attack is the best form of defence.
4. Extremes meet.
5. While there's life, there's hope.

109 Que pouvez-vous dire des phrases ci-dessus pour justifier l'emploi de l'article Ø ?

110 Complétez sur le modèle donné ci-dessous.

EXEMPLE : Green is a mixture of blue and yellow.

1. Orange is a mixture of …
2. Brown is a mixture of …
3. Grey is a mixture of …
4. Pink is a mixture of …
5. Light yellow is a mixture of …

111 Expliquez la présence de l'article Ø dans les groupes nominaux soulignés.

In warm weather, she walked around the little lake near her apartment with Lex on a string. Sometimes she smiled at other people walking around the lake with dogs at night. It was nice the way dogs made things friendly. It was nice the way people with dogs smiled at her because she had a dog, too. But wasn't it dangerous to talk to strange people in parks, dog or no dog?

112 Donnez les noms de langue formés à partir des noms de pays suivants.

1. … is the language spoken in Germany.
2. … is the language spoken in Ireland.
3. … is the language spoken in Norway.
4. … is the language spoken in Portugal.
5. … is the language spoken in Wales.

113 Dites de quels pays sont originaires les personnes mentionnées dans ces extraits d'un poème d'Ogden Nash et quelle langue ils parlent.

EXEMPLE : The Spaniards ▷ The Spaniards come from Spain and speak Spanish.

There came the Spaniards,
There came the Greeks, […]
There came the Dutch
And the Poles and Swedes, […]
Regal Russians and ripe Roumanians.
There came the French
And there came the Finns,
And the Japanese
With their friendly grins.

Look What You Did, Christopher!, Many Long Years Ago
by Ogden NASH, reproduced with permission of Curtis Brown Group Ltd. London
on behalf of Ogden Nash Copyright © Ogden NASH 1945.

114 Soulignez les noms de pays ou d'entités géographiques qui ne sont pas précédés de l'article Ø mais de l'article *the*. (Vérifiez que vous savez les situer !)

Africa • Atlantic • Belgium • Canada • Congo • Cuba • Ethiopia • Maldives • Mediterranean • New Zealand • Sweden • United Kingdom • United Arab Emirates

115 Localisez les entités géographiques suivantes en les faisant précéder d'un article si besoin est.

EXEMPLE : (the/Ø) Greece ▷ Greece is in the Mediterranean Sea.

(the/Ø) Rocky mountains • (the/Ø) Lake Winnipeg • (the/Ø) Belfast • (the/Ø) Melbourne • (the/Ø) Soweto • (the/Ø) Kalahari desert • (the/Ø) Mount Etna • (the/Ø) Isle of Wight

L'article *a/an*

§ 182-187

116 *A* ou *an* ? Choisissez l'article qui convient.

1. honest proposal 2. one-way ticket 3. honour 4. heroic action
5. hour 6. university 7. heir to the Crown 8. historical landmark
9. European 10. honourable master

117 Faites précéder les noms suivants d'un dénombreur : *a/an* + nom + *of…*

EXEMPLE : advice ▷ a piece of advice

bread • cake • chalk • chocolate • evidence • ice • paper • rice • snow • soap

118 Faites précéder les noms suivants d'un dénombreur : *a/an* + nom + *of…*

dust • earth • glass • laughter • rain • rock • smoke • transport

119 Quelle est la valeur de *a/an* dans les proverbes suivants ?

1. A barking dog never bites. *Chien qui aboie ne mord pas.*
2. A bird in the hand is worth two in the bush. *Mieux vaux tenir que courir.*
3. A mouse may help a lion. *On a toujours besoin d'un plus petit que soi.*
4. There's a time and place for everything. *Chaque chose en son temps.*
5. Where there's a will, there's a way. *Vouloir, c'est pouvoir.*

120 Traduisez.

1. Mon père est menuisier *(joiner)*, ma mère est comptable *(accountant)* et moi, je suis étudiant en droit.
2. Deux fois par semaine, je vais au cinéma avec un ami.
3. Avant d'être jardinier, il a été professeur pendant dix ans.
4. Ce gâteau est dur comme de la pierre.
5. En tant que pilote, permettez-moi ce conseil : vérifiez que vous n'avez pas un pneu à plat *(a flat tyre)*.
6. Elle ne se baigne jamais sans bouée *(buoy)*.

121 Utilisez *such a/an* ou *such ∅*.

1. He seems to be … happy man!
2. I've never seen … stormy weather in August.
3. … useful machine would help me a lot.
4. We had … awful summer that we remained abroad for two months in autumn.
5. How can you manage to see with … dirty glasses?
6. They are debating … great issue that you can't disturb them right now.
7. … light earth must be easy to plough.
8. The emergency required … quick action that he couldn't think twice about it.

122 Intégrez l'article *a/an* si nécessaire.

1. You have such (Ø/a) beautiful garden!
2. What (Ø/a) bunch of (Ø/a) liars!
3. You always have such (Ø/a) heavy luggage!
4. What (Ø/a) bore! *(Quel raseur !)*
5. What (Ø/a) pity you couldn't come!
6. That was such (Ø/a) fun!

123 Transformez les phrases suivantes selon le schéma donné en exemple.

EXEMPLE : This job is too difficult: I can't do it. ▷ It's too difficult a job. – I can't do such a difficult job.

1. This story is too incredible: I can't believe it.
2. This explanation is too abstract: I can't understand it.
3. This trip is too expensive: I can't afford it.
4. This loaf of bread is too hard: I can't cut it.
5. This mountain is too high: I can't climb it.

124 Expliquez la différence de sens entre les paires suivantes.

1. a) I know few people who would agree to do it for you.
   b) I know a few people who would agree to do it for you.

2. a) Few people have arrived yet.
   b) A few people have arrived yet.

3. a) I know little about this subject.
   b) I know a little about this subject.

4. a) There is little water left in the tank
   b) There is a little water left in the tank.

125 Traduisez.

1. Je ne connais que peu de choses sur sa vie.
2. Pour moi, ce n'est pas un vrai médecin.
3. Pourrais-je avoir un peu d'eau froide dans mon café ? Il est trop chaud.
4. Elle n'est pas très bonne cuisinière.
5. J'ai juste quelques petites choses à te dire.
6. Elle m'a reconduit à la maison en un rien de temps.

L'article *the*

126 Lisez à voix haute les groupes suivants et dites si *the* se prononce [ðə] ou [ði].

1. the honest proposal 2. the honour 3. the expensive clothes
4. the hour 5. the university 6. the hospital 7. the horrible mistake
8. the historical landmark 9. the umbrella 10. the I.C.B.M. 11. the C.D.
players 12. the hair 13. the M.P. 14. the ewe *(la brebis)* 15. the hotel

127 Justifiez l'emploi de *the* dans les phrases suivantes à l'aide des éléments ci-dessous.

> a) Renvoie à du déjà dit.
> b) Renvoie à un élément de la situation.
> c) Renvoie à du déjà connu culturel.
> d) Précède un nom déterminé par ce qui le suit.
> e) Renvoie à une généralité.

1. He'd better not sit on **the** floor (…).
2. **The** sky (…) is still overcast.
3. We landed at Gatwick. **The** airport (…) is not too far from **the** city (…).
4. **The** customer (…) is always right.
5. Don't forget to lock **the** door (…).
6. Listen! She is playing **the** piano (…).
7. This is **the** school (…) I went to when I was a kid.
8. **The** best of friends (…) must part.

128 Utilisez soit l'article Ø, soit l'article *the*.

1. (Ø/the) President of (Ø/the) France is meeting (Ø/the) English Prime Minister today.
2. (Ø/the) man who's playing (Ø/the) cello in (Ø/the) orchestra is my husband.
3. (Ø/the) World cup drew (Ø/the) tourists from all over (Ø/the) world to (Ø/the) country.
4. All (Ø/the) people who were able to attend (Ø/the) matches were delighted.

5. Your visit has made (Ø/the) letter I had meant to write superfluous.
6. I like bathing in (Ø/the) Mediterranean and sleeping in (Ø/the) sun.
7. All (Ø/the) people on (Ø/the) strike had gathered in (Ø/the) hall of (Ø/the) building in (Ø/the) Regent Street and no one could get inside (Ø/the) office-block.

129 Intégrez un déterminant : Ø, *a/an* ou *the.*

… sun rose up, at first like … yellow ball, then like … disk of … polished brass. … trees, … cornfields, … farms, … pastures, … horses and … workmen in … fields, all appeared instantly bathed in … soft light. … objects … great distance away, … little towers, … smoking chimneys. Slowly … dew became visible, hanging upon … trees like … ladies' earrings. Soon everything was under … warm stillness.

Adapted from *Alexander* by H. E. BATES.

Les déterminants possessifs § 196-198

130 Intégrez un déterminant possessif en relation avec le contexte.

1. He hoped that … fame and popularity would stop … creditors from asking for … money.
2. "Pleased to meet you! I read … article in *Newsweek* on the plane," I said, and I went on telling him I was fascinated by … style.
3. She took a seat opposite … husband.
4. She was very proud of … house, … furniture, but not much of … husband.
5. I looked at the two women but decided not to make any comment about … make-up or … hair.

131 Intégrez un déterminant : Ø, *a/an, the* ou un déterminant possessif.

1. You're … sort of … young man we want.
2. By … time she came round to … apartment … following afternoon, he had realized … truth.
3. He disappeared into … bathroom. There he cleaned … teeth, dropped … toothbrush into … mug and brushed … hair.
4. Then he returned to … bedroom and threw himself on … bed.
5. … final words as he closed … door behind him were lost in … noise of … traffic.

132 Intégrez un déterminant : Ø, *a/an*, *the* ou un déterminant possessif.

1. ... car skidded across ... gravel in ... front of ... house, coming to ... halt in ... flowerbed just below ... kitchen window.

2. ... second later ... van came crashing into ... back of her car, slamming it against ... wall of ... house and shattering ... glass in ... kitchen window.

3. When she reached ... far end of ... gallery, she became aware of ... office in which ... short, balding man, wearing ... old tweed jacket and ... corduroy trousers, was examining ... picture.

4. His occupation, as described in ... passport, was ... banker.

5. He was ... branch manager of ... Barclays Bank in St Albans, ... Hertfordshire, which in ... banking circles is about ... equivalent of being ... captain in ... Royal Air Force.

133 Intégrez un déterminant : Ø, *a/an*, *the* ou un déterminant possessif. Plusieurs solutions sont parfois possibles.

I knew ... Louise before she married. She was then ... frail, delicate girl with ... large and melancholy eyes. ... father and mother loved her with ... anxious adoration, because some illness, ... scarlet fever, I think, left her with ... weak heart and she had to take ... greatest care of herself. [...] She'd been to all ... best heart specialists in ... world, and they all said that ... life hung on ... thread. But she had ... unconquerable spirit.

Adapted from *Louise* by S. Maugham.

134 Mettez au pluriel.

this man • that day • this mouse • that goose • this news •
that people • this leaf • that chief

135 Mettez au singulier.

1. These coming years will be fantastic.
2. Those crossroads are dangerous.
3. These species are rare.
4. Those analyses are wrong.
5. These phenomena seldom happen.

136 Mettez au singulier.

1. Those barracks have to disappear.
2. These aircraft are too old.
3. Check those data, please.
4. These churches are magnificent.
5. Where have you put those keys?

137 Dans les phrases suivantes, soulignez *this/these*
et dites s'ils sont déterminants ou pronoms.

1. Plenty of refugees come across the border these days.
2. A man needs a drink in this climate to help keep him in shape.
3. Only a small plane stands a chance in these mountains.
4. "Joro, this is Mr Chavasse."
5. What it comes down to is this: you don't trust her.

Adapted from *Year of the Tiger* by Jack HIGGINS.

138 Dans les phrases suivantes, soulignez *that*
et dites s'il est déterminant ou pronom.

1. I'd like to see you as soon as possible, if that's alright with you.
2. If that's all for the moment, we'd better be going, I've got plenty
to arrange before that plane takes off.
3. "Remember to keep that face covered. It's as Gallic as a packet
of Gauloises." "I'll try to remember that."
4. We have our differences from time to time. Nothing more than that.
5. He was again conscious of that slight feeling of nausea.

Adapted from *Year of the Tiger* by Jack HIGGINS.

139 Traduisez.

1. Ces fleurs sont magnifiques !
2. Je ne peux pas porter tous ces livres ! Aide-moi.
3. Tu peux vraiment courir aussi vite que ça ?
4. À cette époque-là, il n'y avait pas d'électricité.
5. Voici mon meilleur ami, Tim Parsons.
6. Je n'aime pas celui-là.
7. Tu me prends pour un traître, c'est ça ?
8. Ceux de Londres arriveront plus tard.
9. Celles que nous avons achetées le mois dernier étaient parfaites.
10. Ceux du premier rang peuvent se lever.

140 Traduisez.

1. In this moonlight, I can fly through the passes with no trouble, and that was always the most dangerous part of the operation.
2. No one would dare to spend a night in the open in this area.
3. It was hard not to like a man like this.
4. It is as simple as that.
5. The peasants worship him and this helps our cause enormously.
6. This little adventure will make most interesting reading.
7. I've heard of this ceremony. It's something few travellers ever see.

Adapted from *Year of the Tiger* by Jack HIGGINS.

Both, the two, either, neither §§ 206-208

141 Choisissez la (les) forme(s) correcte(s).

1. Both (my friend/my friends/of my friend) have married older women.
2. Both (them/of them/they) were students at Eton.
3. (The/a/Ø) both her sons live next door.
4. Jack and Jill have known each other for years. (Both/The two) got married last week.
5. You can see (both/the two) of them walking down the street right now.

142 Choisissez la (les) forme(s) correcte(s).

1. (The two/Both) of these books are novels.
2. That's a good bargain! You can have (both/the two) for less than one pound.
3. My (both/two) parents are teachers.
4. (Both/The two) his parents are painters.
5. They are (both/the two) at my school.

143 Traduisez.

1. Je ne peux pas choisir, je les aime tous les deux.
2. Décide-toi ! Tu ne peux pas épouser les deux : c'est soit l'un, soit l'autre.
3. Mais ils sont tous deux si charmants !
4. Soit tu te maries, soit tu restes célibataire *(single)* !
5. L'un ou l'autre me convient, en fait.
6. Tu peux ne pas te marier. Je ne suis pas marié(e) non plus.
7. Mais mon père et ma mère insistent !
8. Ils ont tort tous les deux.
9. Soit je leur obéis, soit je quitte de la maison.
10. Je suis sûr(e) que tu n'aimerais pas cela non plus !

144 Traduisez et dites si *either* est quantifieur, adverbe ou conjonction.

1. You can take either street to the hospital.
2. She can write with either hand.
3. He's the kind of man you either love or hate.
4. She didn't like him. I didn't either.
5. I've lived in London and Detroit but I don't like either city very much.

145 Choisissez.

1. I feel (both/either) excited and exhausted.
2. They're (both/either) very intelligent or very imaginative.
3. (Both/Either) these books are too expensive.
4. (Both/Either) solutions are wrong.
5. I've never met (both/either) her or her sister.
6. We (both/either) said we would come.
7. There's tea or coffee. You can have (both/either).

146 Choisissez.

1. My children (both/either) have green eyes.
2. Do (both/either) of you know where he is?
3. (Both/Either) you and I like going go the movies.
4. Now she can (both/either) speak and write Japanese.
5. You can't have it (both/either) ways.
(On ne peut pas avoir une chose et son contraire.)
6. You left it (both/either) on the kitchen table or in the living room.
7. My sister and I (both/either) went to England last summer, but my brother didn't.
8. We were treated with (both/either) indifference and contempt.

All, whole, each, every
§ 209-215

147 Intégrez *all* dans les groupes nominaux suivants.

these people • my friends • the papers • those nice things • three men • these new methods • your life • her money

148 Traduisez.

1. All dogs are animals but not all animals are dogs.
2. All the people you have met are friends of mine.
3. All five children are good musicians.
4. All wool tends to shrink.
5. You've had all the fun and they've had all the difficult work.
6. All these letters must be posted before five p.m.
7. They've worked hard all summer.
8. We've been waiting for all that time.
9. They were gone all last week.
10. They arrived in all haste.

149 Traduisez.

1. She doesn't cook all that well.
2. I'd never have thought that you, of all people, would appreciate her.
3. All the spectators applauded the performance.
4. All this is now yours.
5. She was dressed all in white.
6. She was all upset about the bad news.
7. The score was two all.
8. You'll have to work all the harder after two weeks' absence.

150 Traduisez ces proverbes et ces expressions.

1. Tout vient à point à qui sait attendre.
2. Tout est pour le mieux dans le meilleur des mondes.
3. Tout ce qui brille n'est pas or.
4. Tout est bien qui finit bien.
5. C'est tout ou rien.

151 *Whole* ou *all* ?

1. You haven't got (whole/all) day to do it.
2. The (whole/all) school meets together twice a year.
3. On the (whole/all), I'm rather happy.
4. She was (whole/all) smiles when I told her we were going out.
5. (Whole/All) I'm asking for is a little tenderness.
6. This rule applies to drivers as a (whole/all).
7. (Whole/All) I could do was wait.
8. He is the best grammarian in the (whole/all) world.

152 Accordez le verbe entre parenthèses.

1. Each bedroom (have) a shower.
2. Each extra day (cost) ten pounds.
3. Each coming day (be) a new day.
4. Each week (bring) its load of pain and joy.
5. Each one of us (be) concerned by this matter.

153 Dites quelle est la nature de *each* : déterminant ou pronom ?

each coming day • thirty pounds each • each one • each of you
• each of the dogs

154 Formez des phrases correctes en intégrant *every* ou *each*.

1. They (every/each) had a suitcase to carry.
2. (Every/Each) one did as they wanted.
3. I saw those two films last week. (Every/Each) of them has a definite appeal.
4. Take one (every/each).
5. I met her twice. It was (every/each) time a pleasure.

155 Choisissez la (les) bonne(s) solution(s).

1. She works …
• all day • every day • all days • each day

2. Have you given … those present one book?
• all • the whole • each • every

3. … one of us did their best.
• all • the whole • each • every

4. … thing should never have happened.
• all • the whole • each • every

5. Is that … you've done today?
• all • the whole • each • every

156 Remplacez *all* par *every* quand c'est possible
(d'autres changements peuvent intervenir en conséquence).

1. He read all the book in two days.
2. He has read all the novels I have given him.
3. The policemen wanted to know all the details of her timetable.
4. All the money that was left was spent later.
5. All her fellow-students were present at the meeting.

157 Traduisez ces expressions.

1. There is an exception to every rule.
2. You can't please everyone.
3. Everything has an end.
4. There is a time and place for everything.
5. Every man has his faults.

Much, many, enough et leurs équivalents   § 216-225

158 Intégrez l'un des quantifieurs suivants : *much, many* ou *enough*.

1. I'm sorry, I'm in a hurry and I can't give you … time.
2. I know … people in this room.
3. People who work hard always have … courage in life.
4. She is a workaholic and always has … work on her hands.
5. When you are really fed up, you say … is …
6. It requires … courage to jump from that height.
7. She has given away … opportunities.
8. This town is nothing but buildings. There isn't … worth seeing here.
9. I'm full up, I've really had …
10. I like eating and drinking, like … children.

159 Choisissez le quantifieur qui convient.

1. I still have (a lot/a good deal of) to do before dinner.
2. (Many/A great deal of) people have found that movie dreadful.
3. I'm sorry but I have (much/enough) problems already.
4. CDs still cost (a good deal/a lot).
5. (Lots/A good many) people would like to be in your situation.
6. (A good deal of/Much) their work is going to be published.
7. There's (many/plenty) more gravy for those who're not on a diet.
8. There's (many/enough) water left for a bath.
9. You shouldn't put so (plenty/much) salt in the water when you boil eggs.
10. There isn't (a lot of/much) I can do about it.

Some   § 226-231

160 Dans les énoncés qui suivent, dites si *some* est déterminant, pronom ou adverbe.

1. Some people had arrived earlier.
2. They were born some twenty years ago.
3. Could I borrow some money?
4. Would you like some more tea?
5. Some like it hot.
6. Some Mr Johnson came this afternoon.
7. "Would you care for some coffee?" "Oh yes please, I'd like some."

8. The house was some twenty miles from the sea.
9. Some would say this is unacceptable.
10. Some of them knew the truth but refused to speak.

161 Dans les énoncés suivants, choisissez entre Ø et *some*.
1. Yes, I'd like (Ø/some) tea, I'd like Orange Pekoe please.
2. I never have (Ø/some) vegetables with meat.
3. He spoke about (Ø/some) Mr Smith I had never heard of.
4. (Ø/Some) people like spending their holidays by the seaside, others in the mountains.
5. That was (Ø/some) meal!

162 Dans les énoncés suivants, indiquez la prononciation de *some* : [sʌm] ou [səm].
1. I had some nice books for Christmas.
2. Some people would appreciate that.
3. Would you like some more coffee?
4. I'll try to visit you some time next month.
5. Some day there will be peace on earth.
6. This really is some champagne!
7. Some friends of yours have phoned today.
8. There's something wrong going on.
9. It's some forty miles from here.
10. She isn't someone reliable.

163 Traduisez en utilisant *some* et indiquez sa prononciation : [sʌm] ou [səm].
1. Si tu en as besoin, il reste de la glace dans le réfrigérateur.
2. Tu sais que tu as laissé de l'argent sur la table du salon ?
3. Certains enfants jouaient au tennis pendant que d'autres se baignaient dans la rivière.
4. Elle lisait une espèce de journal.
5. Ça, c'est un joueur d'échecs.

Any

164 Dans les énoncés suivants, dites si *any* est déterminant, pronom ou adverbe.

1. Is there any living soul here?
2. Can't that car go any faster?
3. You want sweets but I'm afraid I haven't got any.
4. Any car will do so long as I can get there on time.
5. Could any of you boys give me a hand?
6. Is there any politician worth listening to?
7. Do you feel any better now?
8. Not any teacher could teach those pupils.
9. Come any time!
10. I refuse to stay here any longer.

165 Intégrez *some* ou *any* dans les phrases suivantes.

1. I didn't eat ... meat for lunch.
2. We crossed the Channel without ... difficulty.
3. All that is required for the job is ... experience.
4. To avoid ... further delay, passengers are required to board immediately.
5. Are there ... cartridges in that box?
6. They own ... land near a camping site.
7. They say you just have to swallow ... pills and you lose ... weight.

166 Intégrez *some* ou *any* dans les phrases suivantes.

1. Think hard! There must be ... solution to this problem.
2. He was ... good old friend of my father's.
3. I can't see ... good armchair in this room.
4. ... book you have written here!
5. ... fool would know that.
6. I wonder whether ... athlete could have run so fast.
7. "I need ... help." "I'm sorry, I can't give you ..."
8. You can't give a child ... sweets and take them away the next minute.

167 Intégrez *some* ou *any* dans les phrases suivantes, puis traduisez.

1. You want apricots but I don't think there are … left.
2. Tell me how many you have, if …
3. I've made apple pie. Would you like …?
4. I'm sorry but I can't walk … faster.
5. … of the houses were destroyed by the flood.

168 Intégrez *some* ou *any* dans les phrases suivantes, puis traduisez.

1. She gained … two thousand pounds betting on horses.
2. I don't think she will ever feel … better.
3. How about having … more cake?
4. … of his friends are real drop-outs.
5. I refuse to go … farther.

Few, a few, little, a little   § 238-240

169 Associez *a few* ou *a little* avec les mots suivants.

people • water • houses • wine • sheep • time • times • fish • faster
• criteria • chicken • series • mice • love • help.

170 Traduisez.

1. J'ai peu d'amis fiables *(reliable)*.
2. J'ai un peu peur de lui.
3. J'ai quelques bonnes raisons de ne pas l'aimer.
4. Tu ne pourrais pas conduire un peu plus vite ?
5. Cela te demandera un peu de patience.

171 Traduisez.

1. Il reste quelques problèmes à résoudre.
2. Donne-moi quelques explications.
3. Je vois trop peu de gens en ce moment.
4. J'ai trop peu de temps libre pour passer quelques jours avec toi.
5. Je sais peu de choses sur elle.

No, none, nothing

172 Complétez à l'aide de *no, none* ou *nothing*.

1. She speaks very good English and she's ... fool.
2. I got ... sleep last night.
3. Two is company but three is ...
4. It occurs to me that ... ordinary man would be able to speak Chinese so perfectly.
5. You don't get something for ...

173 Complétez à l'aide de *no, none* ou *nothing*.

1. This is ... of your business.
2. It's got ... to do with politics.
3. He shivered for ... accountable reason.
4. This girl had a strange effect, like ... woman he'd known before.
5. Something is better than ...

174 Complétez à l'aide de *no, none* ou *nothing*.

1. Ask ... questions and hear ... lies.
2. Believe ... of what you hear and half of what you see.
3. A bad excuse is better than ...
4. There's ... so deaf as those who will not hear.
5. There is ... new under the sun.

Les nombres
§ 245-247

175 Écrivez en toutes lettres.

137,000 people • 0.9143 • 40,000,000 inhabitants • 3.7853 • 0.394 • 2.205 • 378 • 499 • 219.98 • 29,028

176 Associez les mesures dans les deux systèmes et lisez-les à haute voix.

Système anglo-saxon
an inch • a foot • a yard • a mile • an acre • a pint • an ounce • a pound • a stone • a gallon
Système décimal
1,609 km • 40,47 a • 28,35 g • 30,48 cm • 453,59 g • 0,57 l • 0,914 m • 3,785 l • 6,35 kg • 2,54 cm

177 Associez les mesures dans les deux systèmes et lisez-les à haute voix.

Système décimal
1 cm • 1 m • 1 km • 1 l • 1 kg • 1 cm^2 • 1 ha • 1 km^2 • 1 cm^3 • 1 m^3
Système anglo-saxon
0.386 sq.mile • 1.1760 pint • 219.98 gallons • 0.155 sq.inch • 0.621 mile • 0.394 inch • 0.061 cubic inch • 3.280 ft • 2.205 lb • 2.471 acres

178 Lisez et écrivez en toutes lettres les numéros de téléphone suivants.

00 44 18187498523
00 44 01634556588
00 33 10356065079
00 33 02326007057

179 Traduisez en toutes lettres les dates suivantes.

le 3 novembre 1953
le 17 octobre 1985
le 21 mai 1979
le 27 mars 1988
le 11 janvier 2008
le 2 septembre 2018

L'emploi des prépositions
§ 248-249

180 Intégrez la préposition manquante : *from, by, for, in, to, on.*

1. It's only two weeks … my birthday.
2. They asked me to write a cheque … a hundred pounds.
3. I've just read an article … the *Times*.
4. All philosophers are embarked … a quest … knowledge.
5. I've lost the key … the garage.
6. She has developed an interest … African art.
7. The workers … strike were asking for a rise … wages.
8. There's a solution … every problem.
9. They are twins and it's difficult to tell the one … the other.
10. I missed the late train … Norwich.
11. Have you ever been … a tour of London … night?
12. She's secretary … the manager.

Le génitif
§ 250-257

181 Formez des génitifs à l'aide des deux séries de mots suivantes.

> France • the children • my parents • the President • Jenny and Peter • Dickens • Ulysses • today • anyone

> travels • foreign policy • men • wedding party • novels • toys • weather report • friends • guess

182 Dites si le génitif sert à exprimer la possession, la durée, une unité de temps ou l'appartenance à une catégorie.

1. She was wearing a man's clothes
2. The man's trousers were dirty.
3. He wanted to buy a woman's hat.
4. All that was needed was a year's experience.
5. She was holding a policeman's six-shooter.
6. He didn't attend last week's meeting.
7. I could hear a woman's footsteps on the pavement.
8. His novels' success was not surprising.
9. She was a rich man's wife.
10. Britain's hooligans are unfortunately very famous.

183 Complétez en utilisant un génitif.

EXEMPLE : John has received a letter. I've opened …
▷ I've opened John's letter.

1. My brother has yellow eyes. I like …
2. I've got the newspaper published today. I've got …
3. I visited the cathedral dedicated to Saint Peter. I visited …
4. Merlin worked magic. I admire …
5. Dublin has a fair city center. I visited …

184 Complétez en utilisant un génitif.

1. I've got the same eyes as my father. I've got …
2. Mary wrote a book. I've read …
3. Spielberg has made many films. I love …
4. He was imprisoned for ten years. He was sentenced to …
5. I have bought a knife looking like those of butchers. Have you seen …?

185 Dites où l'on peut trouver les marchandises suivantes en associant les mots des deux séries. (Il est bien sûr interdit de répondre : *at the supermarket* !)

EXEMPLE : You can find fish at a fishmonger's.

jewels • flowers • chicken • tomatoes • shoes • material • cigarettes •
meat • hats • medicine • thread and needles • pans • tins

haberdasher • jeweller • butcher • ironmonger • chemist •
shoemaker • draper • grocer • hatter • greengrocer • florist •
poulterer • tobacconist

186 Dites quel est le nom sous-entendu dans les génitifs soulignés.

EXEMPLE : Tim's parents and Lucy's had never met. ▷ Lucy's parents

1. My brother's in-laws are far nicer than my sister's.
2. I've never been to the dentist's.
3. St John's is famous for heart surgery.
4. I didn't find anything interesting at the jeweller's.
5. Ulysses's were incredible adventures.
6. Is this bike the lady's?

187 Traduisez.

1. He is out of harm's way now.
2. The poor woman's two young children were slightly wounded in the crash.
3. That monster had goat's legs and raven's wings.
4. It took us a whole day's work.
5. My father's mother's favourite activity was going to the bookseller's.
6. That friend of Jenny's has got a demon's eyes and an angel's face.
7. For God's sake, can't you behave!
8. Have you ever been to Sotheby's?

188 Transformez les expressions soulignées en génitifs quand c'est possible.

1. Let me introduce the two young children of the chieftain.
2. I'd been hoping that the workers of that contractor could help me build my house.
3. The nurse had finished bandaging the head of the wounded man.
4. There was an expression of tremendous joy on the man's face.
5. This is the way of the world.
6. The hospital room had that particular smell of disinfectant.
7. She had examined every article of clothing carefully.
8. No one could have got her knowledge of the situation.
9. The victory of the French was a surprise.
10. They had now reached the end of the corridor.

189 Traduisez les expressions soulignées.

1. Le problème de ce garçon, c'est la timidité.
2. Tous attendaient avec impatience la fin du siècle.
3. Le vin de l'an dernier était meilleur.
4. Attention ! Tu vas abîmer le pied de la table.
5. C'est le devoir d'une mère que de protéger ses enfants.

La formation des noms composés

190 Associez les mots composés au développement qui convient.

> milk chocolate • chocolate milk • malt whisky • whisky malt •
> a race horse • a horse race • a vegetable garden • garden
> vegetables • bag leather • a leather bag

> a bag made of leather • vegetables that grow in a garden • whisky
> made with malt • leather used to make bags • a garden where
> you grow vegetables • milk flavoured with chocolate • a race for
> horses • malt used to make whisky • chocolate made with milk •
> a horse that runs in races

191 Expliquez le nom composé en utilisant une paraphrase.

EXEMPLE : a teacup ▷ a cup for tea ;
a landowner ▷ a person who owns land

address-book • bank account • daydream • fingertip • handshake •
money box • leather coat

192 Mettez les mots composés suivants au pluriel.

a mouse-trap • an on-looker • a corkscrew • a grown-up •
a race-horse

193 Traduisez.

a blood transfusion • an oak forest • a story-teller • a dining-room •
an all-day session

Les adjectifs épithètes   § 262-267

194 Intégrez les adjectifs entre parenthèses dans les groupes nominaux soulignés. Attention à l'ordre des mots.

1. This was another of <u>her ideas</u>. (crazy)
2. His discovery aroused <u>interest</u> in <u>circles</u>. (considerable) (various)
3. Your invention has <u>no application</u>. (practical/conceivable)
4. He soon returned to <u>his love</u>, mathematics. (greatest)
5. The car was parked in the driveway of <u>a house</u>. (white-painted/pleasant)
6. He looked at <u>the peaks</u> of the mountains. (white/great)
7. <u>A calm</u> took possession of him. (strange/fatalistic)
8. <u>Her dress</u> was down to her ankles. (woollen/long)
9. They sat down on <u>the bank</u>. (high/grassy)

195 Remettez dans l'ordre les mots entre parenthèses.

1. The (tall/French/seventeen-year-old/handsome) boy was shaking hands with a girl.
2. A (tiny/wooden/cane/rather common) chair stood in front of a magnificent huge stone fireplace.
3. Why don't you buy this blouse instead of that (grey/flannel/old-fashioned) shirt?
4. He drove a (brand-new/black/sports/flashy) car along the Boulevard.
5. For my birthday my friend gave me a (very/rather/leather/expensive/black/large) bag which I could never have afforded to buy.

Les adjectifs attributs   § 268-272

196 Traduisez et dites si les adjectifs sont attributs ou épithètes.

1. Tout ceci n'est que pure coïncidence.
2. Pourriez-vous dire quelque chose de gentil pour changer ?
3. Cette première édition du roman est tout à fait unique.
4. C'est tout à fait impossible, désolée.
5. Son visage était un peu trop blanc.
6. C'était un projet bien trop ambitieux !
7. Fais attention, j'ai une aussi bonne mémoire que toi.
8. Ces abricots ne sont pas assez mûrs *(ripe)* pour être mangés maintenant.

9. Ne t'en fais pas, c'est arrivé par le plus grand des hasards.
10. C'est une question trop compliquée pour moi.

197 Chassez l'intrus.
1. chief • main • essential
2. available • sheer • possible
3. satisfied • content • happy
4. enormous • huge • much

198 Traduisez les paires suivantes.
1. a full wine glass – a glass full of wine
2. the only room available – the only available room
3. the people concerned – the concerned people
4. the involved explanation – the explanation involved
5. You met the proper person. – You met the person proper.

Adjectifs et prépositions §§ 273-284

199 Intégrez la préposition requise par l'adjectif.
1. I was very angry … myself … being such a fool.
2. She was so afraid … spiders she had nightmares when she saw one.
3. Being jobless he felt anxious … his future.
4. The teacher was cross *(en colère contre)* … the pupils.
5. She was really cross *(mécontente de)* … his permanent lies.
6. He had lost all that was dear … him in life.
7. The jobless are often desperate *(vouloir à tout prix)* … work.
8. He had suffered so much that he had sworn to get even *(rendre la pareille à)* … her one day.
9. The old woman was grateful … him … helping her cross the street.
10. The trees are heavy … fruit this year.

200 Choisissez l'adjectif qui convient à la structure de la phrase.
1. Don't be so (angry/nasty) to your little sister!
2. Everything she saw around her seemed (new/sheer) to her.
3. He was so (unconscious/oblivious) to danger that he did incredible things.
4. This palace has never been (designed/open) to the public.

5. She was absolutely (full/petrified) with horror during that film.

6. I can't lend you any money, I'm (short/pressed) for cash at the moment.

7. I was very (proud/happy) of my daughter when she managed to walk again after her accident.

8. My son is very (fair/quick) at figures and mental arithmetic.

9. The witness said he was (reliable/sure) of what he had seen.

10. He was (anxious/scared) of not waking up after the operation.

Les adjectifs en V-*ed* ou V-*ing* §285

201 Complétez. Attention à la forme du verbe.

EXEMPLE : It's **amazing** that you should be here, I (be)… ▷ I am **amazed**!

1. The circus artists were really amusing, all the people present (be) …

2. All the spectators found the acts astonishing, even someone as blasé as my brother (look) …

3. The news is always so depressing that the most optimistic of the viewers can't help (feel) …

4. The howling of the wind was so frightening that hours later I still couldn't sleep. I (be) so …!

5. The subject of his conference was so interesting that I went to see him at the end and told him how … I (be).

6. I found the results of the test worrying and I saw on the doctor's face that he too (feel) …

7. This story-teller is so fascinating that anybody listening to him (grow) …

8. The lesson was so boring that even the most attentive pupils (get) …

Les adjectifs composés §286

202 Complétez les phrases suivantes en utilisant des adjectifs composés.

EXEMPLE : A subject that people know well is ▷ well-known.

1. A baby that his mother feeds well is …

2. Cakes that are made at home are …

3. A girl who has long legs is …

4. Someone who has good manners is …

5. If something breaks you heart, you feel … because it is …

6. A country which produces corn is a … country.

7. A car that looks expensive is an … car.
8. If a story seems never to end, it's a … story.
9. If a woman uses her left hand only, you say she is …

203 Terminez ces phrases en utilisant des adjectifs composés de mesure.

EXEMPLE : A session that lasts four days is a ▷ four-day session.

1. A rest that lasts ten minutes is a …
2. A holiday that lasts two months is a …
3. A man who is fifty years old is a …
4. A magazine that has forty pages is a …
5. A tank that holds sixty litres is a …
6. An answer that is worth two thousand dollars is a …
7. A walk that covers ten miles is a …

Les adjectifs substantivés   § 287-293

204 Transformez les éléments soulignés en adjectifs substantivés.

EXEMPLE : Poor people, homeless people, destitute people are all needy people. ▷ The poor, the homeless, the destitute are all needy people.

1. People who can't see, can't hear, can't speak are said to be disabled people.
2. Black people can still be discriminated against by white people.
3. There's always more than a generation gap between young people and old people.
4. Some films are forbidden to young people under fourteen.
5. People living in Wales are as British as people living in England.

205 Traduisez.

1. Certaines places de parking sont réservées aux handicapés.
2. Les sans-abris sont de plus en plus nombreux aujourd'hui.
3. Trois jeunes sur quatre aiment aller au cinéma.
4. Ce qui est difficile est fait immédiatement, l'impossible prend un peu plus de temps.
5. Les muets ne peuvent communiquer avec des aveugles par le langage des signes.
6. Darwin a exposé *(expounded)* sa théorie de la « survie des plus aptes *(fit)* » dans un livre intitulé *De l'origine des espèces*.

Le comparatif d'égalité : *as/so... as* § 294-298

206 Introduisez un comparatif d'égalité entre les énoncés suivants en tenant compte des éléments entre parenthèses.

EXEMPLE : He is funny./She is funny *(négation)*
▷ He is not as *(ou* so) funny as she is.

1. His hair was black./A raven's wing is black. *(négation)*
2. My sister works in a hospital./My father works in a hospital. *(même)*
3. Her necklace is long./My necklace is long. *(deux fois plus)*
4. I make mistakes./My neighbour makes mistakes. *(autant)*
5. I've had sweets./My little sister has had sweets. *(quatre fois moins)*
6. She likes going to the theatre./He likes going to the theatre. *(autant)*

207 Traduisez.

1. N'achète pas ce livre, il est quatre fois plus cher ici que dans l'autre librairie.
2. J'ai autant d'amis que toi.
3. Elle n'est malheureusement pas aussi intelligente qu'elle en a l'air.
4. Elle parle un aussi bon anglais qu'un présentateur *(announcer)* de la BBC.
5. Pourrais-tu parler deux fois moins vite pour que je comprenne deux fois plus rapidement ?
6. Par ce temps, nous sommes aussi bien ici que dehors.
7. Je ne pense pas qu'elle soit si fâchée que cela.
8. Arrête de faire toujours la même chose que moi !

Les comparatifs de supériorité et d'infériorité § 299-313

208 Insérez la forme correcte du comparatif de supériorité.

1. I'd be (happy) if I had less work.
2. Could you give me something (spicy) and (tasty)?
3. She is far (intelligent) than you think.
4. I couldn't get any (near) because of the traffic getting (heavy) all the time.
5. She must be his (old) sister since there were only two of them.
6. He looked (angry) than hurt.
7. I have never seen a (smashing) car.
8. If the door was (narrow) you would get more space here.

209 Écrivez les comparatifs de supériorité des adjectifs suivants.

big • fat • wide • deep • high • narrow • feeble • heavy • handsome • right • true • good • wrong • bad • real • thin • meagre • acid • fair • old

210 Traduisez.

1. Si tu n'es pas plus soigneux *(careful)* à l'avenir, je ne t'achèterai plus rien.
2. C'est bien plus facile que vous ne le pensez !
3. Si tu veux mon avis, elle est plus bête *(stupid)* que méchante *(nasty)*.
4. Je n'ai jamais connu quelqu'un de plus riche que lui.
5. Tout ceci me semble plus réel désormais, j'avais peine à y croire.
6. Ton intuition *(insight)* est plus juste que tu ne le crois.
7. Je n'irai pas plus loin, j'ai les jambes plus fatiguées que le reste.
8. Il n'a pas voulu que j'en lise plus.
9. Ils sont arrivés plus tard que les autres mais n'ont pas été les derniers.
10. J'ai vu Tim et Tom la semaine dernière : le premier a grossi, le second a maigri *(grow + adjectif au comparatif)*.

211 Récrivez les mots entre parenthèses sous forme d'accroissements ou de diminutions progressifs en fonction du contexte.

EXEMPLE : Professional cycling is getting (criticized).
▷ Professional cycling is getting more and more criticized.

1. It's getting (hard) to find someone you can really trust.
2. His speech was so long that the audience felt (interested).
3. Means of communication are becoming (quick).
4. It was pouring outside and I was (in a hurry) to leave.
5. Going on holiday costs (money).
6. Village schools have (pupils). Some will have to close.
7. She was (pleased) as she heard the nice speech of the manager.
8. (People) use the Internet.
9. The imaginary world was getting (real).
10. There are (hitchhikers) on the roads these days.

212 Complétez en utilisant les comparatifs des adjectifs ou adverbes entre parenthèses. (Attention, *more* est à la fois le comparatif de *much* et de *many* !)

1. The ... I know you, the ... I appreciate your company. (much – little)
2. The ... he earns, the ... he spends. (much – much)
3. The ... she gets, the ... she is. (old – beautiful)
4. The ... her clothes, the ... they suit her. (dear – little)
5. The ... you try, the ... it is. (hard – good)
6. The ... friends he has, the ... he feels. (many – happy)
7. The ... you come, the ... we leave. (early – soon)
8. The ... he loves her, the ... she loathes him. (much – much)
9. The ... drinks you have, the ... you become. (many – dangerous)
10. The ... he goes, the ... chances he has of coming back. (far – few)

213 Traduisez.

1. Better be envied than pitied.
2. Better late than never.
3. The grass is always greener on the other side.
4. The more, the merrier.
5. Prevention is better than cure.
6. The sooner begun, the sooner done.

Les superlatifs   § 314-319

214 Terminez les phrases avec l'un des éléments ci-dessous utilisé à la forme qui convient.

(of/in/Ø) I know. • (of/in/Ø) the day. • (of/in/Ø) the world. •
(of/in/Ø) Congress. • (of/in/Ø) I have ever heard. •
(of/in/Ø) the history of literature.

1. This is the nicest piece of news ...
2. He is the most famous senator ...
3. That's the worst place ...
4. China is the most populated area ...
5. It's the strangest remark ...
6. This is the best ever book ...

Les pronoms personnels

§ 320-333

215 Transformez le complément souligné en pronom.
Attention à l'ordre des mots.

1. He used to bring flowers <u>to his wife</u> every other day.
2. The milkman brought milk <u>to the Johnsons</u> every morning.
3. Could you give my share <u>to my children</u>?
4. All her friends gave presents <u>to Mary</u> for her child's birth.
5. She had promised a few things <u>to her husband</u> so that he would not go.
6. I send my best regards <u>to yours parents</u>.
7. They never showed their holiday photographs <u>to John</u>.
8. I had to teach linguistics <u>to crowds of students</u>.
9. He was supposed to tell the truth <u>to the jury</u>.
10. She gave it <u>to her best friend</u>.

216 Transformez les phrases suivantes en utilisant le discours indirect.

EXEMPLE : She said: "All I know is that they don't like me."
▷ She said that all she knew was that they didn't like her.

1. She wondered: "I don't know whether I should go or stay with you."
2. She asked: "Can you give me a hand, the two of you?"
3. They said to me: "You should be more careful! You have hurt your leg again!"
4. He said to them: "Mind your own business from now on."
5. She started by saying: "In this novel, I have tried to show what my life was in those days."
6. She shouted to him: "You'd better hurry or we'll be late!"

217 Traduisez.

1. « Personne d'autre que toi ne sait où elle se trouve, alors c'est toi qui vas aller la chercher. »
2. « Qui a acheté tout ceci ? – C'est moi. – Toi ? – Oui, c'est moi qui suis allée faire les courses. »
3. « Je ne les ai pas encore rencontrés. Et toi ? – Moi, je les ai vus hier. »
4. « J'en ai assez de lui ! Il me tape sur les nerfs ! »
5. « Il est trois fois plus gros qu'elle et pourtant, elle mange deux fois plus que lui. »
6. « On sonne. Cela doit être elle. Elle est toujours en retard quand elle vient chez nous. »

7. « Comment s'appelle ton chat ? – Kitty. Elle est très indépendante. »

8. C'est son père qui veut lui parler au téléphone, mais elle n'est pas là et il ne va pas me croire quand je vais le lui dire !

9. « Qui a dit : "On ne sait jamais" ? – Ce que je sais, c'est que ce n'est pas moi. »

10. « Nous arrivons de New York. – Enchantés. Nous, nous arrivons de Cuba. »

218 Traduisez. Précisez la catégorie d'emploi de *it* (reprise, annonce, impersonnel, après un verbe d'appréciation).

1. It's important that you should know it.
2. I won't be able to come to your wedding and I apologize for it.
3. It was very difficult for me to believe you didn't know it either.
4. It's very kind of you to do it for me.
5. I thought it best to tell you about it first.
6. It doesn't matter, besides, I really don't care (about it).
7. It was obvious that nobody found it essential to sell it.
8. If it is really so easy to do, why don't *you* do it?
9. It's always he who speaks last that is right.

Les pronoms possessifs § 334-340

219 Complétez à l'aide des pronoms possessifs en utilisant les indices fournis.

1. I don't think this is … (my car) although … (my car) is the same colour and the same make.
2. That friend of … (you have friends) is no match to … (my friend).
3. She had taken one of … (their books) in order not to write on … (her book).
4. You have never met that doctor of … (we have a doctor) I told you about.
5. … (your hair), … (their hair) and … (his hair) have nothing in common.

220 Traduisez.

1. That self-styled doctor of yours strangely looks like ours, don't you think?
2. She was looking at me with those smiling eyes of hers.

3. Take theirs if you haven't got yours, but no way will I lend you mine.

4. Bring your children along, mine will be delighted to play with yours.

5. Theirs is a very beautiful house, nothing in common with his!

221 Traduisez.

1. Nothing serious! He's just a friend of mine…

2. Have you told that husband of yours to hurry up? Because of that laziness of his, we'll be late!

3. That diamond of mine, as you say, is far more authentic than hers.

4. His hair is naturally curly, not mine.

5. Between yours, theirs and mine, I'll always prefer my own children.

Valeurs de *one* § 341-351

222 Traduisez.

1. One day you will understand that it is better to have one reliable friend than ten good pals.

2. I'd like one gorgeous red rose, please. It's for the one woman in my life.

3. You said one million, not one million two hundred? How could you make such a mistake?

4. My one and only leisure activity is playing a game of squash from time to time.

5. She had twins. One is a boy, the other a girl. They both have a beauty spot on their right cheeks.

6. Which peaches do you want? Green ones and unripe ones as usual?

7. My car is too small, I'll have to buy a bigger one.

8. One and one and one is three.

223 Mettez au pluriel les mots soulignés. Attention à l'accord des verbes.

1. I don't know all of them. I only know this one.

2. This blue one and that green one will do.

3. I'd rather have the one that is in the shop-window.

4. This one looks very much like the one I borrowed from you.

5. The one I like has nothing in common with that ugly one.

Traductions de « on »

§ 352-356

224 Traduisez.

1. On aurait dû te prévenir de mon retard !
2. On y va ? Êtes-vous prêts ? Dépêchez-vous ou on va rater le début du film !
3. Alors on est content de son voyage, petit ?
4. On a eu un temps épouvantable au mois de juillet !
5. On t'a appelé au téléphone ce matin.
6. À la direction, on dit qu'on va licencier les deux secrétaires.
7. On m'a demandé de faire ce rapport pour demain.
8. On s'est bien amusés hier. Et toi, qu'as-tu fait ?
9. On dit dans la presse que trois personnes ont été grièvement blessées.

225 Traduisez en utilisant « on » en français.

1. You'd never think it rained so much last summer.
2. He is said to have been made to confess to crimes whose authors had never been found.
3. It was stolen while you were sleeping! Have you never been told to lock your door?
4. You know, we never know what the future has in store for us.
5. I had been told I would get a crew cut but they didn't touch my hair.

226 Traduisez en utilisant « on » en français.

1. We'll try to prove that two and two is not always four.
2. One should never say such things to someone who is depressed!
3. We'll be waiting for you outside the station at eight sharp.
4. So there are things you want to tell me? What shall we start with?
5. People always say that a friend in need is a friend indeed and that is absolutely true.

227 Intégrez un pronom personnel ou réfléchi en fonction du contexte.

1. Look at …, John! You've been jumping in puddles again!
2. She spends considerable time looking at … in the mirror.
3. They really enjoyed … at the party last night.
4. You should think about … first.
5. What's happened to …? You look terrible!
6. Take care of … . I'll come and see the three of you next week.

228 Intégrez un pronom personnel ou réfléchi en fonction du contexte.

1. While he was trying to get … ready, his son kept fidgeting *(n'arrêtait pas de gigoter)*.
2. Whenever they thought about …, they regretted their absence.
3. Their daughter … was present at their wedding.
4. I think you can easily do it … without any help.
5. He didn't have any money on … so he couldn't even pay for …
6. What do you reproach … for? You didn't do it!

229 Reformulez les phrases suivantes à partir de l'amorce proposée en utilisant un pronom réciproque.

1. John kept looking at Mary and Mary kept looking at John.
John and Mary …
2. Brothers love their sisters and sisters love their brothers.
Brothers and sisters …
3. She congratulated him on his degree and he congratulated her on hers.
They …
4. We have never met them and they have never met us.
We …
5. I send him letters and he sends me letters.
We …

230 Traduisez et dites si le segment souligné a un emploi réfléchi ou réciproque.

1. Plus je pense à nous et plus je me dis que nous devrions <u>nous</u> voir moins souvent.
2. Ils ont perdu le dernier match et <u>s'</u>en veulent énormément *(be annoyed with)*.

3. Elle a honte d'elle-même.

4. Il n'y a rien de mieux que d'essayer de s'entraider.

5. Les gens parlaient entre eux et je ne pouvais pas me faire entendre.

6. Votre livre se vend bien, vous pouvez être fiers de vous.

7. Détends-toi, dors dix minutes et quand tu te réveilleras,
tu te sentiras très bien.

8. Je vais me féliciter moi-même si personne d'autre ne le fait !

9. J'ai rencontré le président en personne et il s'est intéressé
à ce que je faisais.

10. Elle a appris toute seule à jouer du piano.

La phrase

Les phrases affirmatives et négatives § 369-372

231 Reformulez les phrases en les commençant par l'adverbe souligné.

EXEMPLE : I shall <u>never</u> forget what he did for us.
▷ Never shall I forget what he did for us.

1. It had <u>hardly</u> been raining when the hurricane hit the house.
2. I understood <u>only then</u> what he was saying.
3. We shall <u>never</u> forgive them for what they did.
4. I have <u>often</u> complained about it, but to no use.
5. I have <u>seldom</u> seen so much happiness.

232 Reformulez les phrases en commençant par l'amorce indiquée.

EXEMPLE : It only occurred to me then that he was in love with me.
Only then … ▷ *Only then did it* occur to me that he was in love with me.

1. As soon as she left her home the sun started shining.
No sooner …
2. There has never been such a disaster before.
Never before…
3. I was so angry that I decided to write a letter to the director.
So angry …
4. My anger was such that I became speechless.
Such …
5. The boss was to be seen nowhere.
Nowhere …
6. He arrived late and he didn't even apologize.
Not only … but …
7. His conduct was so absurd that they all laughed.
So …
8. I have never had such an idea before in my life.
Never before in my life …
9. I remember your grandmother well.
Well …
10. You are to talk about it on no account.
On no account …

233 Traduisez en anglais les réponses en utilisant *so* ou *neither*.

EXEMPLES : I knew him well. *Moi aussi.* ▷ So did I.
I've never liked that writer. *Elle non plus.* ▷ Neither (*ou* nor) has she.

1. "I've passed my exams!" « *Moi aussi.* »
2. "You've got wonderful eyes!" « *Toi aussi.* »
3. "I can't stand that guy." « *Eux non plus.* »
4. "You've put on weight." « *Toi aussi.* »
5. "He looked ill." « *Son amie aussi.* »
6. "We'll manage." « *Nous aussi.* »
7. "She often thinks about it." « *Sa mère aussi.* »
8. "He can't remember." « *Pierre non plus.* »
9. "I worked very hard." « *Les autres aussi.* »
10. "That's something we had never considered." « *Nous non plus.* »

234 Reformulez ces phrases en *if* à l'aide de *had* ou de *should* (style soutenu).

EXEMPLES : If I had known, I would have called you. ▷ Had I known,
I would have called you.
If ever you left earlier, it would not be a problem. ▷ Should you leave
earlier it would not be a problem.

1. If he had arrived earlier the problem would have been solved
immediately.
2. If ever she arrived now we would still have time.
3. If he had had a better idea, things would have been different.
4. If ever you changed your plan, please let us know in advance.
5. If it started raining now we would have to cancel our project.
6. They would not be here, if they had passed their exams.

235 Traduisez.

« Peut-être est-il trop tard pour commencer notre réunion.
– Il est en effet trop tard. Aussi pouvons-nous décider de partir.
– Mais voilà notre chef.
– Désolé, il y avait tellement de camions sur la route ! Parmi eux se
trouvait même un tracteur ! Jamais je n'oublierai ce cauchemar. À peine
avais-je quitté la maison que les ennuis commencèrent. Si j'avais su, je
ne serais pas sorti de chez moi.
– Nous non plus. »

236 Mettez en relief l'élément souligné à l'aide de *it is…/it was…*

1. <u>Annabel</u> wrote a love story when she was ten.
2. Annabel wrote <u>a love story</u> when she was ten.
3. Annabel wrote a love story <u>when she was ten</u>.
4. <u>You, Mr President</u>, are telling us a lie.
5. You, Mr President, are telling <u>us</u> a lie.
6. You, Mr President, are telling us <u>a lie</u>.
7. <u>We</u> understood what he did at that moment.
8. We understood <u>what he did</u> at that moment.
9. We understood what he did <u>at that moment</u>.

237 Reformulez ces phrases en commençant par *What* et en ajoutant *is/was*.

EXEMPLE : Ben bought a car. ▷ What Ben bought <u>was</u> a car.

1. Sophie's looking for a new apartment.
2. Steve wanted a cheeseburger.
3. She broke a vase.
4. They will like Brooklyn Bridge.
5. She has visited New York.
6. I might see the parade in London.
7. They want to buy three copies of that book.
8. He says that he's never felt that way before.
9. Errol is sticking to the idea that life is for living.
10. I've never understood what they liked about him.

Les phrases interrogatives   § 373-382

238 Transformez les phrases suivantes en interrogatives.

EXEMPLE : Tracey is at home. ▷ Is Tracey at home?

1. She can speak German.
2. He will go to New Zealand next year.
3. You're going out tonight.
4. The unemployment rate has come down in Britain.
5. They prefer tea to coffee.
6. Your parents never leave their country.
7. They have a nice house.
8. They would rather stay inside.
9. Steve has many brothers and sisters.
10. Brenda said she'd be late.

239 À partir des phrases interrogatives obtenues, répondez aux questions par l'affirmative puis par la négative. Utilisez l'auxiliaire qui convient.

EXEMPLE : Is Tracey at home? ▷ Yes, she is./No, she is not.

240 Transformez les phrases suivantes en interrogatives, en commençant par le mot interrogatif indiqué.

1. Something happened. *What …?*
2. You were doing something last night. *What …?*
3. Somebody rang. *Who …?*
4. Somebody wants some more tea. *Who …?*
5. She went somewhere. *Where …?*
6. They looked at something. *What …?*
7. You did it in a certain way. *How …?*
8. They arrived at a certain time. *When …?*
9. Somebody left a note on my desk. *Who …?*
10. Omar lived in California then. *When …?*

241 Posez des questions à partir des phrases proposées, en remplaçant *something, someone* et *some time* par un mot en *wh-*.

EXEMPLE : You are looking at someone. ▷ Who are you looking at?

1. You sent the flowers to someone.
2. He relied on someone.
3. They cared for someone.
4. Carey was listening to something.
5. She was thinking about something.
6. He thought of someone.
7. We both laughed at something.
8. You sent for someone's doctor.
9. The hooligans broke into someone's house.
10. You said he would be back some time.

242 Transformez les questions suivantes en interrogatives indirectes en utilisant l'amorce indiquée.

EXEMPLE : When will he come back? *I wonder …* ▷ I wonder when he will come back.

1. "Where are they going?" *Their friends wonder …*
2. "Who called?" *Laurie wants to know …*
3. "When will you see her again?" *I'd like to know …*

4. "Who was on the phone?" *Let's ask them* ...
5. "How old are her grandparents?" *Peter wants to know...*
6. "What did they buy?" *I'd be pleased to know* ...
7. "Why are you crying?" *I'm asking you* ...
8. "What were you listening to?" *I'd be interested to know* ...
9. "How did you manage it?" *I'm just asking* ...
10. "Why did she run away?" *Could you tell me* ...

243 Transformez les questions suivantes en interrogatives indirectes en utilisant l'amorce indiquée. Attention à l'emploi des temps après un verbe au prétérit.

1. "What were they doing at this time yesterday?" *The policeman asked* ...
2. "Which of these books did she like best?" *The librarian wanted to know* ...
3. "Why did Louise lie to him?" *She enquired* ...
4. "Where will you spend your holiday?" *She forced him to tell her* ...
5. "Who have you been seeing?" *He was furious and asked her* ...

244 Ajoutez un adjectif ou un adverbe après *how*, en vous aidant de la notion donnée entre parenthèses.

1. How ... is the lake? (depth: *profondeur*)
2. How ... is your sister? (age: *âge*)
3. How ... is the Tower of London? (height: *hauteur*)
4. How ... do you go to New York? (frequency: *fréquence*)
5. How ... brothers and sisters do you have? (quantity: *quantité*)
6. How ... money can you lend me? (quantity: *quantité*)
7. How ... are you planning to stay here? (duration: *durée*)
8. How ... is it from London to Manchester? (distance: *distance*)
9. How ... is the swimming pool? (length: *longueur*)
10. How ... is the road? (width : *largeur*)

245 Dites si l'expression *how long* exprime une longueur dans le temps (une durée) ou dans l'espace (une dimension).

1. How long is the lake?
2. How long are you planning to stay here?
3. How long did you live with her?
4. How long is the new car he's just bought?

5. How long have you been learning Spanish?
6. Did they tell you how long they stayed in South Africa?
7. How long ago did their family arrive in Britain?
8. How long have they been married?
9. I wonder how long he is going to talk.
10. How long did it take you to drive to Manchester?

Dans quelles phrases pourrait-on remplacer *how long* par *since when* ?

246 Traduisez les phrases de l'exercice 245.

247 Les équivalents de « comment ». Traduisez.
1. Alors, comment allez-vous aujourd'hui ?
2. Sais-tu comment est sa mère ?
3. Comment sais-tu qu'il ne viendra pas ?
4. Comment se fait-il qu'il ne t'ait rien dit ?
5. Comment l'as-tu su ?
6. Comment pourrais-je lui faire comprendre ?
7. Comment veux-tu que je le sache ?
8. Comment l'a-t-elle fait ?
9. Tu peux me dire comment il est, ce type ?
10. Comment ferons-nous ?

248 Complétez à l'aide de *what* ou de *which*.
1. … did he say?
2. Hello! … would you like?
3. You don't want to see him? … do you mean by that?
4. … time did they leave?
5. … of these meals do you recommend?
6. … is the matter with him?
7. … will you tell her when you see her?
8. … sentence should I rewrite in my essay?
9. I have too many sweaters. … one should I wear?
10. … will you be wearing tonight?

249 Complétez à l'aide de *what*, de *which* ou de *who*.

"Hi, Phil! It's me, Linda."

"… 's that?"

"Linda."

"Oh, … do you want?"

"I just wanted to say 'Hi'!"

"… do you mean, 'Hi'! Do you know … time it is?"

"… does it matter? I have so much to tell you, Phil."

"Look, why don't you call another one of your friends?"

"… one?"

"I don't care … one. Just call … you want."

"OK, of John, Peter and Steve, … should I call?"

"That's your business, not mine. Talking of … , could you lend me your car?"

"… one? The Rover or the Mercedes? But … happened to your own car?"

"It broke down and I desperately need one, Linda."

"That's *your* business, honey, not mine. Bye."

250 Traduisez.

1. Quel temps fait-il ?
2. Comment ils sont, ses parents ?
3. Comment vont tes parents ?
4. Depuis combien de temps sont-ils en Allemagne ?
5. À qui est ce livre ?
6. Ils sont en Écosse pour combien de temps ?
7. Il y a combien de temps qu'il n'a pas plu ?
8. Mais enfin, tu n'as pas vu cette voiture ?
9. Je me demande dans quelle mesure il est vraiment déterminé à réussir.
10. Quelles chances a-t-elle de réussir son permis de conduire ?

Les phrases exclamatives

§ 383-387

251 Modifiez les phrases à l'aide du mot donné entre parenthèses.

EXEMPLE : It was difficult. (how) ▷ How difficult it was!

1. It was nice to see you. (how)
2. She has changed over the years. (how)
3. You are a sweetheart. (what)
4. Your cousin is nice. (how)
5. He was a fool not to listen to her advice. (what)
6. This tea is hot. (how)
7. It was a relief to see them. (what)
8. This programme is stupid. (how)
9. It feels strange not to be with my daughter. (how)
10. He made a fuss *(faire des histoires)* about nothing. (what)

252 Modifiez les phrases à l'aide du mot donné entre parenthèses.

EXEMPLE : I was stupid. (so) ▷ I was so stupid.

1. It was great to see you. (so)
2. I behaved in a stupid way. (such)
3. I have to study. (so much)
4. It hurts to listen to you. (so much)
5. She was mad at him. (so)
6. I was a fool to believe you. (such)
7. He really cares for you. (so much)
8. I'm sorry but I am in a hurry. (such)

253 Reliez les deux phrases à l'aide du mot entre parenthèses.

EXEMPLE : It rained. We left a week earlier. (so much)
▷ It rained so much that we left a week earlier.

1. There were mistakes. I couldn't read his paper. (so many)
2. We had terrible weather. We decided to leave after an hour. (such)
3. I was in a hurry. I didn't notice the accident. (such)
4. The book was funny. I couldn't stop reading. (so)
5. I was late. It was useless to try to make it. (so)
6. They were given wine to drink. They got drunk in less than an hour. (so much)
7. It rained. We decided to cut short our holiday. (so much)
8. It was a lousy film. We didn't watch it to the end. (such)

254 Complétez les phrases à l'aide de *what (a), how, so, so much, so many* ou *such (a)*.

1. … fool I was not to listen to her advice.
2. … nice to see you!
3. Chris was in … hurry that she forgot to call you.
4. I have to work … hard to please them.
5. … lovely this is!
6. There were … people you could hardly move.
7. He has … hair on his chest that he looks like a bear.
8. His admiration for your art is … great that he'd pay any price for it.
9. They have … to offer us.
10. I cannot stand … bad manners.

255 Reformulez ces phrases en faisant une interro-négative exclamative. Puis traduisez.

EXEMPLE : He is sweet. ▷ Isn't he sweet! *Comme il est charmant !*

1. They speak well.
2. They behaved badly.
3. I'm smart.
4. I know.
5. It's clever.
6. He is old now.
7. She looks sweet.
8. Time flies. *(Le temps passe vite.)*

V + *to* + V, V + V-*ing*, V + base verbale § 388-396

256 Mettez le verbe entre parenthèses à la forme qui convient :
to + verbe *ou* V-*ing*.

EXEMPLE : She wants (leave) tomorrow. ▷ She wants to leave tomorrow.

1. If you choose (leave), please let us know.
2. I swear (tell) the truth.
3. We all enjoyed (travel) together.
4. He promised not (talk) to Joan's neighbours again.
5. I can't stand (drive) on motorways.
6. We spent all our time (wait) for him!
7. I advise you (listen) very carefully.
8. I just love not (have) to go to work!
9. I expect him (give up).
10. I told my parents not (worry).

257 Mettez le verbe entre parenthèses à la forme qui convient.

When it was too late he decided (tell) his Mum about his secret love affair. He knew how (not/shock) her and wanted (be cautious) with her so as (not/cause) any problem. He is very sweet and hates (hurt) people's feelings but at the same time he couldn't bear (not/let her know). So he asked her (promise) (not/talk) while he was speaking. He had to wait for (she/sit up) in her bed and then started (explain) that he disliked (she/pry) into his affairs and that he enjoyed (lead) his own life. He kept (talk) never daring (look) at her. When he stopped (speak) he realized that she was sound asleep.

258 Construisez une phrase à partir des éléments proposés, en employant *to*, V-*ing* ou la base verbale.

EXEMPLE : I want … (they must leave immediately).
▷ I want them to leave immediately.

1. I advise … (you shouldn't write that letter).
2. They swear … (they never stole that bike).
3. They swear … (they will never steal again).
4. My parents have always let … (I can do anything I want).
5. I was listening very carefully. I heard … (she whispered to her husband).

6. I distinctly remember … (he took your keys).

7. I would prefer … (I won't see her right now).

8. I like … (I listen to opera).

9. I would like … (I listen to an opera).

10. I promise … (I will not do it again).

Récapitulatif § 388-396

259 Traduisez.

1. Peux-tu m'aider à remplir ce formulaire ?

2. Si tu choisis de rester, il faudra coopérer.

3. J'aime qu'on m'admire. J'aimerais tant qu'on m'admire.

4. Je veux que tu me dises la vérité.

5. Tu refuses de me dire où il est ?

6. Vous étiez tous d'accord pour voir ce film, non ?

7. Finalement, on l'a persuadée de nous accompagner.

8. J'attends que ses amis arrivent.

9. Ils ne supportent pas qu'on les touche.

10. Ses parents ne le laisseront pas partir.

260 Traduisez.

1. Ils font semblant de ne pas me voir.

2. Inutile de me dire comment ça marche.

3. Ça ne me dérange pas de ne pas y aller.

4. Il n'a pas arrêté de pleuvoir.

5. Je l'ai entendue chanter.

6. Je ne sais pas comment le lui dire.

7. Les clients avaient l'intention de boycotter ce produit.

8. Essaie de te concentrer, pour changer.

9. Prendre ce train, cela veut dire voyager pendant quinze heures.

10. Je regrette de ne pas en avoir parlé.

Les équivalents de « faire » § 398-400

261 Complétez les phrases à l'aide de *make*, *have* ou *get* au temps qui convient.

1. It'll take time but I'll … Mustapha to give you a hand.
2. He … us work extremely hard and we don't regret it now.
3. I'll … him call you.
4. I … this cake made especially for you.
5. She … him park his car on a double yellow line.
6. I'll … him do the dishes tonight.
7. Don't worry, I'll … my brother to write your essay for you.
8. This actor always … me laugh.
9. You'll … me blush if you go on like that!
10. As a child I … my brother write my essays for me.

262 Traduisez.

1. J'ai fait peindre ma chambre par mon frère.
2. Faites frire le poisson dans un peu d'huile.
3. On m'a fait ouvrir ma valise. (emploi du passif)
4. Ne vous en faites pas, je vous ferai aider par un policier.
5. Me suis-je fait comprendre ?
6. J'ai essayé en vain de me faire obéir.
7. Il s'est fait voler sa montre.
8. Il y avait beaucoup de circulation et cela fait que je suis arrivé en retard.
9. L'idée l'a fait sourire.
10. Ils m'ont fait boire de la vodka.

263 Traduisez.

1. J'ai réussi à lui faire ranger son fouillis *(clear up his/her mess)*.
2. Maman a fait venir le médecin.
3. Je vous le ferai savoir dès que possible.
4. Ça y est, j'ai fait réparer la voiture.
5. Ils se sont fait couper les cheveux.
6. Les pauvres, ils se sont fait avoir par leur avocat.
7. Toutes ces belles histoires font rêver.
8. Le prince fit reconstruire le château.
9. Quand j'étais petit, mon père me faisait faire mon lit tous les matins.
10. N'essayez pas de me faire croire qu'il est ici.

Les constructions résultatives

§ 401-405

264 Combinez les deux phrases en une seule puis traduisez.

EXEMPLE : I have painted my bathroom. Now it is red.
▷ I have painted my bathroom red.
J'ai peint ma salle de bains en rouge.

1. She has washed her car. Now it is clean.
2. Jo shouted last night. Now, her voice is hoarse.
3. Steve read a lot. Now he is almost blind.
4. She ran quickly and then she was out of the shop.
5. They starved and then they died.
6. They starved themselves and then they died.

265 Combinez les deux phrases en une seule, à l'aide de *into, out of* ou *to*.

EXEMPLE : Dad talked to me. So I made an appointment with my dentist.
▷ Dad talked me into making an appointment with my dentist.

1. They blackmailed her. So she had to resign.
2. They threatened her. So she had to sign the document.
3. My mother tricked me. So I picked up my aunt at the airport.
4. Erwin talked to Sue. So she didn't accept the offer.
5. The President clearly fooled the State Secretary. So the State Secretary supported the resolution.
6. Sheila argued. So Betsy didn't become a nurse.
7. His parents begged him: he should not marry the girl.
8. My dad persuaded me. So I did a degree in maths.

Les coordonnants § 406-408

266 Traduisez.

1. Elle est à la fois maire et ministre.
2. Ils ne savent ni lire ni écrire.
3. Soit vous restez et vous m'écoutez, soit vous partez et vous pouvez faire ce que vous voulez.
4. Non seulement j'avais raison mais tous les autres avaient tort.
5. Si tu téléphones et que je ne suis pas là, laisse un message.

267 Soulignez les coordonnants et relevez les segments coordonnés.

The Duke recognized the strategic importance of the castle, which was mentioned for the first time in the twelfth century. It lay at the junction of major trading routes: the wheat and wine route (from north to south) and the salt and silver route (from west to east). When it came into the possession of the Duke, it was given to his son, who had it rebuilt. During a battle, the Duke's son held out against attacks for more than a month, but the castle was finally pillaged and burnt. Five centuries later, the castle was given to the town of Rigmarole, which offered it to the Prince of Mornmouth and his young and beautiful wife. The Prince asked an architect if he could either restore it or build a new one. He replied that he would restore it but that he would do it slowly and meticulously, so that it would take ten or fifteen years. In the end, both he and the Prince had to wait twenty years before the dream came true.

La subordination § 409-410

268 Soulignez les propositions subordonnées dans le texte suivant.

Dear John,

I suppose that you'll be using my bedroom while you're in London. I'm afraid I've lost the key to the large cabinet that is next to the bed. So if you have anything confidential you should keep it under the carpet, as no one will think of looking there. You can use my books, which are all in my bedroom, though I'd appreciate if you wouldn't lend them to anyone, as books are rarely returned. I have been told by Carey, who came round last night, that you intend to give a party during your stay in London. It's all right with me but make sure that nothing gets broken and that everything stays clean. You know I hate coming back to a dirty house.

Les pronoms relatifs

§ 411-424

269 Dans ce texte, entourez les pronoms relatifs et soulignez l'antécédent.

The Duke, who was getting old, recognized the strategic importance of the castle, which was mentioned for the first time in the twelfth century. It lay at the junction of major trading routes: the wheat and wine route (which ran from north to south) and the salt and silver route (which ran from west to east). When it came into the possession of the Duke, it was given to his son, who had it rebuilt. During a battle, the Duke's son held out against attacks which were led by the Duke's arch-enemy, for more than a month. But the castle whose walls were not thick enough, was finally pillaged and burnt. Five centuries later, the castle was given to the town of Rigmarole, which offered it to the Prince of Mornmouth and his young and beautiful wife. The Prince asked an architect, whom he had known for years, if he could either restore it or build a new one. He replied that he would restore it but that he would do it slowly and meticulously, so that it would take ten or fifteen years. The roof, whose tiles were imported from Italy, took longer than he thought. In the end, both he and the Prince had to wait twenty years before the dream came true.

270 Dans le texte précédent, justifiez l'emploi des pronoms relatifs.

EXEMPLE : The Duke, **who** : antécédent humain, pronom relatif sujet.

271 Réunissez les deux phrases à l'aide du pronom relatif.

EXEMPLE : The solid table was consumed in a few minutes. It had stood thirty years in the same place. ▷ The solid table that had stood thirty years in the same place was consumed in a few minutes.

1. My mother pushed her neighbour roughly forward. My mother was a relatively aggressive person.
2. We lived in a street. It contained a garage called Ever-Ready.
3. We lived in a street. Its name was Langdon Park Road.
4. It was a narrow room. It had two windows between two wings of the building.
5. Once in a while she appeared with something. That thing took you by surprise.

6. My uncle was always generous. He had never married.

7. The house is old. We live in it.

8. The man was on television last night. His photograph is in my wallet.

9. Brian asked me a lot of questions. He's a police inspector.

10. The shop belongs to my husband. I'm walking towards it.

272 Ajoutez le pronom relatif qui convient. Si plusieurs possibilités existent, précisez-le.

1. The friends with … we play tennis live in our neighbourhood.

2. The friends … we play tennis with live in our neighbourhood.

3. Marsha, … had always refused to marry, suddenly decided to embark on a new life.

4. This is the book … I told you about and … you must read at once.

5. He's given me four bottles of perfume, none of … I like.

6. Sandy, … uncle I am, never forgets my birthday.

7. This is the best show … I have ever seen.

8. This is the only car … will do 60 miles per hour in 10 seconds.

9. The Japanese, … language is not well known outside Japan, tend to learn English, … is now a universal language.

10. The government had not cut the interest rate since 2008, after … investors chose other investments.

273 Dans les phrases suivantes, relevez les pronoms relatifs, les propositions relatives et les antécédents.

EXEMPLE : As I said before, there were several beggars in the street. The one who walked like a prince asked for a cigarette.
▷ *Pronom relatif :* who – *relative :* who walked like a prince – *antécédent :* The one

1. The medicine is Amilile, the same that women use regularly.

2. The darkness was thin, like some old dress that has been worn and worn for many winters.

3. The artist left after shooting the woman who no longer wanted to live with him.

4. On the desk were two novels which she had received as Christmas presents.

5. The other book was one that she actually lived with.

6. The music came from records that dated from the 1920s.

7. I was a poet who had a job in a coffee shop.

8. These records were souvenirs of our father, a man whom we barely remembered, a man whose name was never mentioned.

Traduction des pronoms relatifs §419-424

274 Les équivalents de « dont ». Traduisez.

1. Voici la personne dont je pense qu'elle serait un bon candidat.

2. Je n'aime pas du tout la façon dont il conduit.

3. Que faire de ces livres dont personne ne veut ?

4. Ce musée possède de nombreuses peintures, dont une seule est du xxᵉ siècle.

5. L'histoire, dont je me souviens bien, est moins intéressante que le style.

6. Elle possède plusieurs voitures dont une seule est utilisable.

7. Ce dont je me rends compte, c'est qu'il n'est jamais trop tard.

8. Ce dont je suis fier, c'est de mon accent.

9. Il a acheté une maison ancienne, mais dont le toit est tout neuf.

10. Les amis dont je te parle n'habitent pas ici.

275 Dans les phrases suivantes, que pouvez-vous dire de l'antécédent ? Traduisez le pronom relatif *which*.

1. He became a drug addict, which is not surprising.

2. That was the end of my third section, which means that I can now move on to my conclusion.

3. You've always loved him, which not many have done.

4. My boyfriend has been offered a new job, which implies that we cannot stay in this town.

276 Les équivalents de « ce qui… », « ce que… ». Traduisez.

1. Ce que je regrette, c'est qu'il ne m'en ait pas parlé.

2. Ruth a toujours refusé de m'en parler, ce que je regrette.

3. Ce qu'elle m'a dit ne te regarde pas.

4. Ce qu'ils veulent, c'est qu'on les laisse tranquilles.

5. Tu vois ce qu'il y a là-bas ?

6. Ce qui est regrettable, c'est qu'il ne s'en rende pas compte.

7. Aller les voir ? C'est précisément ce que je refuse.

8. Ils sont tous partis avant la fin du match, ce qui est vraiment incroyable.

9. Ce qu'il te faut, c'est une nouvelle montre.

10. Il est arrivé avec ce qui ressemblait à une voiture.

277 Traduisez en faisant appel à un relatif + *ever*.

1. Qui m'aime me suive.

2. J'irai où tu iras.

3. Nous pouvons partir quand tu veux.

4. Quiconque sait faire cet exercice a tout compris.

5. Quel que soit l'endroit où nous mangeons, il n'est jamais content.

6. De toutes ces voitures, vous pouvez choisir celle que vous préférez.

7. Nous ferons tout ce que tu voudras.

8. Le premier d'entre vous qui trouve la bonne solution aura droit à mon estime.

Subordonnées en V-*ing* sujets § 425

278 Remplacez *it* par une proposition sujet en V-*ing*. Dans quelle phrase aurait-on pu utiliser *to* + verbe ?

EXEMPLE : They complain all the time. It is unbearable.
▷ Their complaining all the time is unbearable.

1. Melvin was late. It annoyed Michael.
2. Henry passed his exam. It rejoiced his parents.
3. I failed my exam. It did not sadden my boyfriend.
4. They hesitated. It could have been dangerous.
5. She rang five minutes after the accident. It puzzled the policeman.
6. He left a note. It didn't make things easier.

279 Traduisez les phrases obtenues.

Subordonnées en V-*ing* compléments § 426-428

280 Réunissez les deux phrases en une seule, à l'aide de V-*ing*.

EXEMPLE : I hate something.– I am late. ▷ I hate being late.

1. Do you mind something? – I leave right now.
2. Jane remembers something. – She wrote a letter of complaint to her boss.
3. He left without something. – He did not say goodbye.
4. After something the minister decided to resign. – She failed to convince the prime minister.
5. Thank you for something. – You listened with so much interest.
6. I don't object to something. – You smoke in here.
7. My students are used to something. – They travel a lot.
8. I prefer his new habit to something. – He woke up very late.
9. We all look forward to something. – Errol visits us soon.
10. They were busy. – They were repairing their old car.

Ø ou *that* ?   § 429-432

281 Utilisez la conjonction Ø ou *that* pour introduire la proposition subordonnée. Préférez la conjonction Ø à *that* à chaque fois que cela est possible.

1. I knew … it would be too difficult.
2. He always said … you were the best.
3. Phil told me … he would be late and … we needn't wait for him.
4. Did she know … you were married?
5. I think, if I am to judge by his performance, … he is our best hope for a medal.
6. Don't worry, I will tell him … you called.
7. They supposed, after hearing all the witnesses, … the suspect was not among them.
8. I believe … he is out, but I can check if you insist.
9. Joan thought … you were American.
10. Vivien said … , as it had not snowed for quite a few days, they would not go skiing.

Équivalents des subordonnées françaises   § 429-430, 437

282 Traduisez ces phrases qui comportent « trouver » + adjectif.

1. Elle trouve bizarre qu'il n'ait pas téléphoné.
2. Je trouve inquiétant qu'elle ne réponde pas.
3. Vous trouvez normal qu'ils soient partis aussi rapidement ?

283 Traduisez ces phrases qui comportent en français des propositions infinitives.

1. Elles se sont plaintes de ne pas être écoutées.
2. Je doute de pouvoir vous répondre.
3. Ils disent vouloir vous aider.
4. Je pense aller à Édimbourg demain.
5. Vous imaginez vous en tirer *(get away with it)* comme ça ?
6. J'admets ne pas savoir comment faire.

284 Traduisez ces phrases qui comportent des propositions conjonctives sujets.

1. Qu'il n'arrive que demain est surprenant.
2. Qu'il ne pleuve qu'une fois par an ici me paraît bizarre.
3. Qu'il m'en veuille est normal.

4. Qu'elle n'arrive pas à se décider est compréhensible.

5. Qu'il n'ait pas téléphoné m'inquiète.

6. Qu'ils aient aimé Wagner n'est pas si facile à comprendre.

285 Traduisez ces phrases qui comportent « d'autant plus que... ».

1. Il le regrettera d'autant plus qu'un jour je serai riche.

2. Je ne sais pas comment elle va. D'autant moins qu'elle ne m'écrit plus.

3. C'est d'autant plus dangereux que tu ne sais pas conduire.

4. Ce test est d'autant plus facile pour Sean qu'il est en anglais.

Emploi des temps   § 432, 434, 442

286 Mettez le verbe entre parenthèses à la forme qui convient.

1. They insisted that she (start) her job immediately.

2. It's incredible that she (be) so arrogant.

3. It's vital that they (be) here as soon as possible.

4. Mum suggested that we (go) swimming this afternoon.

5. I strongly recommend that you (remain) quiet for a moment.

6. So, what does the doctor suggest we (do)?

287 Traduisez.

1. Il est incroyable qu'elle ait dit ça.

2. Il est surprenant qu'une telle chose se soit produite.

3. Il n'est pas normal qu'ils se soient comportés ainsi.

4. Il est regrettable que vous vous soyez disputés.

288 Mettez le verbe entre parenthèses à la forme qui convient.
Puis traduisez les phrases ainsi obtenues.

1. I'll phone you as soon as I (get) home.

2. He said he would come as soon as he (drive) Karen home.

3. We'll buy a new TV set when our old one (break down).

4. My parents said we'd buy a new TV set when our old one (break down).

5. We'll leave when you (finish) your work.

6. We're moving to Miami next month. Come and visit us whenever you (want).

7. The judge said she would invite the press once her investigation (be) over.

8. I know he'll arrive when it (be) too late.

289 Reliez les deux phrases à l'aide de *no sooner... than...*
ou *hardly... when...*

EXEMPLE : She had left him. He started crying. ▷ No sooner had she
left him than he started crying. *ou* Hardly had she left him when
he started crying.

1. I saw her. I stopped my car.
2. It started raining. We left the beach.
3. She called. They started laughing.
4. We got off the plane. We were gripped by the cold.
5. I began accelerating. My husband screamed at me.

290 Mettez le verbe de la principale à la forme qui convient.

1. If I had known, I (not come).
2. He (not go) if it starts raining.
3. The examiners (cancel) the exam if they had been told about
the cheating.
4. Brenda (not talk) to Kevin if she had known the truth.
5. If he comes with his grandparents we (not be able to) go climbing.
6. If you arrived two days earlier you (can) meet my new girlfriend.
7. If you pass your exam I (take) you to the restaurant.
8. If you ever passed your exam I (take) you to the restaurant.

291 Mettez le verbe de la subordonnée en *if* à la forme qui convient.

1. Imagine all the things we could do if you (be) here with me.
2. If you (make) an effort I'm sure you would succeed.
3. I might have married her if things (be) different.
4. If the president (not be) so rash she would have been reelected.
5. They can come to my party if they (behave oneself).
6. She could make it if ever she (apply) her energy to it.

Récapitulatif

292 Complétez chaque phrase avec une des propositions de l'encadré.

1. He insisted on trying again …
2. They looked at each other …
3. We'll leave …
4. The government will negotiate …
5. Take my advice: don't get married …
6. The path runs around a corner …
7. No sooner had he met her …
8. You may borrow my car …
9. The students enjoy this novel …
10. You may have any of my books …

- as soon as it stops raining.
- all the more as it is easy to read.
- provided you bring it back with a full tank.
- until you are over 30.
- where it turns out of sight.
- than he offered to marry her.
- as long as you take good care of them.
- even though he knew it was useless.
- if they stop striking.
- as though they had never met.

Dans quelles phrases ainsi obtenues peut-on inverser l'ordre des deux propositions ?

Tell ou say ?   § 445

293 Remplacez *say* par *tell* et *tell* par *say*. Apportez les modifications nécessaires. Attention ! C'est impossible dans deux phrases. Lesquelles ?

1. She told me nothing.
2. Unfortunately, they did not say anything to their parents.
3. He told you lies.
4. The headmaster said to the assembly that discipline should be encouraged.
5. Stop telling everyone that you're my boyfriend!
6. They told their best friends that they did not want to get married.
7. You keep telling the same jokes over and over again!
8. Say it to the teacher before it's too late.

294 Employez *say* ou *tell* à la forme qui convient.

1. He ... : "Good morning."
2. Has he ... you where he would spend his holiday?
3. I'm only ... aloud what everybody is thinking.
4. He ... me something that made me laugh.
5. You should ... the truth and nothing but the truth.
6. There's something I want to ... you.
7. This is a free country, I can ... what I want.
8. She ... me how happy she was.
9. Would you mind ... me your name and address?
10. Could you ... that again, please?

Discours indirect : question, conseil, ordre...   § 446-449

295 Transformez les questions en subordonnées à l'aide de l'amorce indiquée.

EXEMPLE : Do you have a driving licence? *The policeman asked me ...*
▷ The policeman asked me if I had a driving licence.

1. "So, do you want to marry him or not?" *My mother enquired ...*
2. "Did you have a nice meal?" *She asked me ...*
3. "Have you lost anything?" *He wondered ...*
4. "Are you going out tonight?" *She wanted to know ...*
5. "Will the children be home for dinner?" *My husband asked ...*
6. "Has the minister resigned yet?" *The neighbour wondered ...*

296 Transformez les questions en *wh-* en subordonnées
à l'aide de l'amorce indiquée.

1. "Where did you meet him?" *She asked …*
2. "When will you be back?" *She enquired …*
3. "What did he say to you?" *They wanted to know …*
4. "Why was Chris late?" *John wondered …*
5. "Who has gone?" *They asked …*
6. "How did it happen?" *She wondered …*
7. "Where are they?" *The judge wanted to know …*
8. "When are they coming back?" *Their mother asked …*

297 Récrivez les phrases suivantes en utilisant l'amorce indiquée.
Quand plusieurs possibilités existent, signalez-les.

1. "Shut up" he said. *He ordered …*
2. "Open your books on page 43." *She asked …*
3. "Never say you're sorry." *He advised …*
4. "You should go to the cinema." *He suggested …*
5. "I'm sorry I didn't warn you." *The guest apologized …*
6. "Don't lie to me." *She told … /She forbad(e) …*
7. "Don't park your car here." *The policeman warned …*
8. "Why don't you come round for tea?" *She invited …*

Emploi des temps au discours indirect § 450-453

298 Passez au discours indirect en utilisant l'amorce indiquée.

EXEMPLE : "The train leaves at 5:32." *She said…*
▷ She said the train left at 5:32.

Au présent
1. "We want to go to Disneyland." *The children cried …*
2. "John and William never write to us." *Mr and Mrs Litten complained …*
3. "It's too late to catch the train." *He said apologetically …*

Au prétérit et au *past perfect*
4. "I met the man of my dreams yesterday." *She announced …*
5. "Anyway, Liz had never trusted Al." *Her mother explained …*
6. "If John came two days earlier it would make things simpler."
They insisted …

Au *present perfect*

7. "I've come to say goodbye." *The boy said ...*
8. "I've decided to get a divorce." *The President's wife cried ...*
9. "Sorry, Miss, you've just missed your train." *The station master told Kirstie ...*

Renvoi à l'avenir

10. "Mr Byrd will be here in a moment." *The secretary explained ...*
11. "I shall not speak to her." *Her former husband exclaimed ...*
12. "Things will get better." *The clairvoyant predicted ...*

Modaux

13. "Thomas, you must come in at once." *Mother told Thomas ...*
14. "I can swim that length in 30 seconds." *Michele bragged ...*
15. "You could stand up when I come in." *The headmaster shrieked ...*

299 Passez du discours direct au discours indirect en utilisant l'amorce.

1. "He is going to New York." *He asserted ...*
2. "I've made a mistake." *She acknowledged ...*
3. "It's too late to react." *He admitted ...*
4. "We've never been invited." *They confirmed ....*
5. "I'll probably move to London in September." *He answered ...*
6. "I've got no time to lose." *She objected ...*
7. "Nick, you're too stupid for the job." *The boss shouted ...*
8. "I didn't have the courage to talk to her." *Alex accepted ...*

300 Transformez ces phrases de dialogue en discours indirect.
Attention aux pronoms personnels.

"Henry, have you found anyone who can help me?" asked Nathalie.
"I've found a priest who will be able to help you. His name is Father McCrory. Go to him. He may be able to tell you something," Henry replied.
"Thank you. I suppose that will help."
"Do you have any relatives around here?"
"Only an aunt."
"Oh! that helps a bit, doesn't it?"
"She had the house in Langdon Park Road."
"Anyway, I feel sure Father McCrory could help you. He knew everybody in this neighbourhood. Try not to be too sad. One never knows."
"I know. Life goes on."

Discours indirect libre

301 Soulignez les exemples de discours indirect libre dans le texte suivant.

Mrs Litten was feeding the fire. Tears rose to her eyes. Why had it happened to her? Did she deserve such a harsh treatment? She had always been kind to everybody and could not understand what was going on in her life. The other women did not say a word but Mrs Litten felt their sympathy. She crept closer to her son and asked him. "Melvin, can you pray?" "No, mother." Mrs Litten could understand her son's feelings. Perhaps he could not pray today because of the pain he felt. In a few days, perhaps next week, he would probably feel differently. He might even break down. That would be terrible. If he broke down, it would take weeks for him to recover. Outside the wind abated as if it feared to disturb the mother and her son.

302 Transposez le texte de l'exercice 301 au discours direct, là où c'est possible, jusqu'à *sympathy* (l. 5), en explicitant les pensées du personnage à l'aide de *she asked herself* ou de *she thought*.

Annexes

Adjectif + préposition

§ 273-282

303 Ajoutez la préposition qui convient après l'adjectif (vous pouvez utiliser un dictionnaire).

1. They were afraid ... the dog.
2. I am angry ... you.
3. They were annoyed ... their children.
4. He is not ashamed ... his parents.
5. I am aware ... the problem.
6. He is very bad ... maths but good ... French.
7. Look, I am bored ... this film.
8. I feel quite close ... my parents.
9. I am crazy ... you.
10. The students were all disappointed ... the new course.

304 Ajoutez la préposition qui convient après l'adjectif.

1. My town is very famous ... its porcelain.
2. I am very fond ... music.
3. This house is full ... mystery.
4. I am furious ... you. Yes, I am furious ... the way you treated your sister.
5. The whole family was glad ... his success.
6. Are you interested ... what I'm saying?
7. He was jealous ... his brother's success.
8. You should be kind ... your sister.
9. I have always been nice ... her.
10. I am pleased .../satisfied ... what you have done.

305 Ajoutez la préposition qui convient après l'adjectif.

1. We are all proud ... you.
2. I am sorry ... what I said.
3. We were surprised ... the way he behaved himself.
4. The judge was tired ... hearing the same excuse over and over again.
5. I am worried ... the future.
6. I am amazed ... his skills.
7. He felt annoyed ... the policeman for being so uncooperative.
8. We are very worried ... our daughter's health.
9. She is busy ... her new job.
10. He is clever ... building miniature boats.

306 Ajoutez la préposition qui convient après l'adjectif.

1. We were delighted ... the news.
2. Even though he is 30 he is still dependent ... his parents.
3. This problem is different ... the other one.
4. I am disgusted ... the way he treated his friends.
5. Everybody was excited ... the news of the victory.
6. I am not yet very familiar ... this new computer.
7. Bess is already fed up ... her new job.
8. I am now frightened ... meeting him in the street.

307 Ajoutez la préposition qui convient après l'adjectif.

1. I am grateful ... you ... telling me the truth.
2. Laurie said she was impressed ... your new book.
3. I don't think Thomas is very keen ... visiting her again.
4. She is mad ... him *(en colère contre lui)* for not telling her that he was married.
5. She still loves him. In fact she is still mad ... him *(folle de lui)*.
6. Why should I be responsible ... my brothers and sisters, when they are so rude ... me? In fact, I am even scared ... them and I am sick ... having to live with them.
7. I am terrible ... driving.
8. That's typical ... him, always on the road.
9. They felt upset ... the news.

Verbe + préposition § 12-13, 456-463

308 Employez la préposition qui convient (servez-vous d'un bon dictionnaire).

1. I often think ... you.
2. We always go ... Spain in the summer.
3. He suffers ... loss of memory.
4. There is no need to hide the truth ... us.
5. The hero managed to escape ... the battle.
6. I would like to apologize ... being late.
7. I didn't steal that car ... anyone. I borrowed it ... Miss Page.
8. Do you know what sea separates England ... France?
9. That country would like to take part ... /to participate ... our games.
10. He will never succeed ... his examination.

309 Employez la préposition qui convient.

1. Could you translate this text ... German for me?
2. You should divide this cake ... six portions.
3. They turned that clever child ... a good-for-nothing.
4. Is this table made ... solid wood?
5. Children depend ... their parents.
6. I could live ... bread and butter.
7. Don't spend all your money ... sweets.
8. We would like to congratulate you ... your victory.
9. Fill it ... petrol to make it work.
10. You should cover your car ... something to protect it.

310 Employez la préposition qui convient.

1. I'm looking ... my keys. I need them to lock the house.
2. Stop laughing ... those poor children.
3. I don't approve ... their behaviour.
4. How much did you pay ... it?
5. Could you comment ... this text?

Place de la préposition
§ 417, 456-457

311 Posez des questions à l'aide de l'amorce indiquée.

EXEMPLE : I sent it to John. *Who* ... ▷ Who did you send it to?

1. I replied with a polite letter. *What* ...?
2. We went to Scotland last summer. *Where* ...?
3. She killed him with a knife. *What* ...?
4. I am in love with Tracy. *Who* ...?
5. We are dependent on our grandparents. *Who* ...?
6. We slept in George's house. *Whose* ...?
7. He is married to my cousin. *Who* ...?
8. I felt more interested in this story. *Which* ...?

312 Reliez ces phrases à l'aide d'un pronom relatif.

EXEMPLE : I know a guy. You've just been talking to him.
▷ I know the guy (who) you've just been talking to.

1. This a book. John is keen on it.
2. I wrote a story. No one is interested in it.

3. She is my cousin. I have often told you about her.
4. They are friends. We depend on them for food.
5. They are former schoolchildren. We are so proud of them.
6. Here is a house. The three men broke into it *(l'ont cambriolée)*.
7. These are rare books. I've been looking for them everywhere.
8. The Smiths are our neighbours. Passers-by keep looking at them.

313 Complétez ces phrases à l'aide des doubles compléments donnés entre parenthèses. Pour certaines, deux constructions sont possibles.

EXEMPLE : Sandy gave ... (a book/Fred). ▷ Sandy gave Fred a book *ou* Sandy gave a book to Fred.

1. The dog brought ... (Peter/two bones).
2. The magician showed ... (the hat/his partner).
3. My parents sent ... (me/a letter) and I left ... (message/Anny).
4. She wants to book ... (a plane ticket/Bob).
5. I'll teach ... (maths/her) and she'll pay ... (it/me).
6. The manager explained ... (the problem/his employees).
7. We'll provide ... (them/enough food).
8. The murderer described ... (his act/the jury).
9. I'd like to remind ... (my friends/the presents I gave them).
10. There is no need to ask ... (him/his help).

Principales prépositions de lieu   § 464-474

314 Retrouvez l'équivalent anglais des prépositions suivantes.

à travers • au-dessus de • le long de • derrière • parmi • au-dessous de • près de • en bas de • à l'intérieur de • à côté de • au large de *ou* séparé de • en face de • devant • autour de • vers

near • inside • opposite • down • above • next to • by • along • past • towards • close to • across • through • among • off • behind • round • below • in front of • over

315 *Across* ou *through* ? Choisissez la préposition qui convient.

1. Let's walk (across/through) that street.
2. They managed to row (across/through) the lake in 15 minutes.
3. This road will take you (across/through) the forest.

4. The teacher drew a line (across/through) the blackboard.
5. Which river flows (across/through) New York?
6. It took five years to build a bridge (across/through) the river.
7. They entered the house (across/through) the large window.
8. He shouted at me from (across/through) the hall.
9. Jason passed his fingers (across/through) Mary's hair.
10. That car drove (across/through) a red light *(a brûlé un feu)*!

316 *At* ou *in* ? Choisissez la préposition qui convient.

1. We met (at/in) a party, not (at/in) the street!
2. I'll pick you up (at/in) the bus stop.
3. They arrived (at/in) the factory half an hour late.
4. Time seems to fly faster when I'm (at/in) work than when I'm (at/in) home.
5. We were (at/in) school together when we were 12.
6. The Kaufmans arrived (at/in) Canada, more precisely (at/in) Montreal, in 2008.
7. We started with an argument but (at/in) the end we became good friends.
8. Would you rather live (at/in) the country *(à la campagne)* or (at/in) town?
9. You either left your bag (at/in) the garden or (at/in) the swimming pool.
10. I have to see my boss (at/in) the end of the week.

317 Complétez par l'une de ces prépositions : *in, to, into, on* ou *onto*.

1. Let's all go ... the pub to celebrate!
2. He walked ... the room majestically.
3. She felt weak and fell ... the floor.
4. You'll find your friends ... the living room.
5. He threw the book ... the fire.
6. Come on! Step ... the platform *(quai)*.
7. The car crashed ... the wall.
8. She threw the keys ... the table.

318 *Among* ou *between* ? Choisissez la préposition qui convient.

1. This ferry sails (among/between) Dover and Calais.
2. There were (among/between) five to seven people.
3. (Among/Between) those present were ten orphans.
4. They had less than 12 dollars (among/between) them.
5. The property was divided (among/between) his wife and himself.
6. The property was divided (among/between) all his grandchildren.
7. (Among/Between) you and me, I must admit that I've never liked her.
8. He is now half way (among/between) youth and middle age.

Principales prépositions de temps   § 475-483

319 Complétez par l'une des trois prépositions : *on, at, in* ou *Ø*.

1. I'll meet you at the station … 3:15.
2. He arrived here … Christmas day.
3. She rang … Wednesday morning to say she'd start working … the next day.
4. I last saw her … Easter, that is, … the 14th of April.
5. I'm usually away … weekends, but you can contact me … the evening.
6. … her arrival, everybody became silent.
7. Tell her I'll be back … a few days, … Monday week (*lundi en huit*) to be precise.
8. They'll come back … three months, that is … August.
9. Nobody was here … time: they were supposed to arrive … the morning.
10. Most of them got here … the afternoon and some even … night!

320 Traduisez le segment souligné en employant *by, from… to, since, for* ou *during*.

1. Je vous attendrai de trois à quatre.
2. Pouvez-vous terminer ce travail d'ici demain ?
3. Que faisiez-vous durant l'été ?
4. Je n'ai pas travaillé de juin à septembre.
5. Téléphonez-moi ce soir au plus tard à 6 heures.
6. Je suis à l'université depuis l'année dernière.
7. Pendant cinq ans il ne nous a pas écrit.
8. Je la vois régulièrement depuis trois ans.

Autres prépositions

§ 484-490

321 Reliez chaque énoncé ci-dessous à un énoncé de l'encadré pour exprimer la cause ou le contraste.

1. Stop dawdling, because of you …
2. Due to a late arrival of the train, …
3. Unlike Ruth …
4. Given their children's reluctance …
5. Considering what Brenda said …
6. Owing to the heatwave …

> - the express to London will leave at 10:05.
> - the sports event was cancelled.
> - we'd better not count on her.
> - I've always liked going to the pub.
> - we may never be in time for our appointment.
> - they decided not to go to New Zealand.

322 Reliez chaque énoncé ci-dessous à un énoncé de l'encadré pour exprimer la cause ou le contraste.

1. Why don't you go out for a walk …
2. They decided to go on foot …
3. We managed to go to New York …
4. What you have done is …
5. The meeting was postponed …
6. She failed …

> - despite her parents' encouragement.
> - thanks to Patty's generosity.
> - in spite of the weather conditions.
> - on account of their being late.
> - contrary to the headmaster's orders.
> - instead of wasting your time watching TV?

323 *As* ou *like* ? Choisissez.

1. I felt … an idiot after what I said.
2. … a teenager he was always very shy.
3. … a professional adviser I strongly support your choice.

4. My father behaved … a child when he saw her.
5. It was exactly … a dream!
6. It fits her … a glove.
7. He now works … an accountant in a famous bank.
8. He drinks … a fish.
9. Don't talk to me … that!
10. It looks … rain. *(On dirait que le temps est à la pluie.)*

324 Traduisez le segment souligné.

1. Ils sont arrivés <u>à pied</u> de la gare.
2. Je l'ai vu <u>à la télévision</u>.
3. Les ouvriers sont <u>en grève</u> depuis lundi.
4. Les choses sont différentes <u>de ce côté-ci de</u> la Manche.
5. Barbara a été <u>au chômage</u> pendant six mois.
6. Elle vit <u>au troisième étage</u>.
7. J'ai dû conduire <u>sous la neige</u>.
8. La maison était <u>en feu</u>.
9. Je suis arrivé <u>en train</u>.
10. Je n'ai pas pu dormir <u>dans l'avion</u>.

Récapitulatif § 456-490

325 Traduisez chacun des segments soulignés en utilisant une préposition.

<u>À mon avis</u>, chanter <u>sous la pluie</u> est une mauvaise habitude. Si vous chantez seul <u>dans la rue</u> ou <u>à votre travail</u>, on vous prendra pour quelqu'un de bizarre. <u>Par exemple</u>, l'autre jour j'ai voulu rentrer chez moi <u>à pied</u> plutôt qu'<u>en bus</u>. J'habite <u>en banlieue</u>, à cinq kilomètres <u>du centre-ville</u>. Je n'étais pas <u>pressé</u>. Il fallait simplement que je sois rentré <u>pour huit heures</u>. Je me sentais <u>en vacances</u>. En passant <u>par le parc</u> qui se trouve <u>en face de la mairie</u>, je me suis mis à chanter un air d'opéra. Tout le monde me regardait de haut en bas, voire se retournait sur moi. <u>Finalement</u>, j'ai dû m'arrêter tellement j'avais <u>peur de</u> ces gens. C'est <u>selon moi</u> une <u>limite à</u> la liberté. D'autant plus que j'ai une belle voix. Je prends des cours de chant <u>depuis seize ans</u>, <u>en fait depuis mon enfance</u>. Quand j'étais enfant, je voulais chanter <u>comme ténor</u>, comme

Pavarotti. Certes, j'en suis loin, malgré tous mes efforts. Mais, entre vous et moi, est-ce si important ?

Quand nous sommes entre amis, ça n'a pas d'importance. D'ailleurs je suis prêt à vous chanter, ma chère collègue, le grand air du ténor de *Turandot*, juste pour vous. Comment ça, « hors de question » ? Vous ne voulez pas m'écouter ? C'est à cause de gens comme vous que la liberté est bafouée. Je serais mieux dans une île déserte qu'au milieu d'ignorants. À Pâques, c'est-à-dire dans deux mois, je donnerai ma démission. Je préfère être au chômage qu'avec vous tous. À votre arrivée en septembre, j'ai pensé que vous étiez mieux que les autres. Comme je me suis trompé !

Place de l'adverbe

§-491-525

326 Dans les phrases suivantes, soulignez les adverbes et dites ce qu'ils modifient.

1. Quite frankly, I have other things to worry about.
2. You're too good to be true.
3. Honestly I didn't say anything against you.
4. I'll always love you.
5. This film is incredibly long and dull.
6. He's still looking for his keys.
7. I read it quite recently.
8. He expressed his opinion convincingly.

327 Mettez l'adverbe à la place qui convient.

1. He is away. (often)
2. She does not answer her mail. (always)
3. I'll write to them. (never)
4. It rains here. (hardly ever)
5. He's complaining about the service. (always)
6. We've enjoyed the show. (really)
7. It can't be true. (possibly)
8. "Won't you call her?" "I will./I will not." (certainly)

328 Récrivez la phrase en commençant par l'adverbe donné dans l'amorce.

EXEMPLE : He left the house and it started raining. *Hardly* …
▷ Hardly had he left the house when it started raining.

1. She opened her mouth and I recognized her voice. *No sooner* …
2. They had never seen such a beautiful show. *Never before* …
3. He had said a few words and he began crying. *Hardly* …
4. The children closed their eyes and fell asleep. *No sooner* …

Place de *all*, *both* et *each*

§ 495

329 Mettez *all*, *both* ou *each* à la place qui convient.

1. We've decided to move to Chicago. (all)
2. They are lodging a complaint against their boss. (all)
3. We are properly married. (both)

4. They have returned to their parents' home. (each of them)
5. We will write soon. (all)
6. They can be quite tiresome. (both)
7. We had cucumber sandwiches for lunch. (each)
8. "I'm fed up with this show." "We are." (all)

Adverbes de manière, lieu, temps, fréquence   § 496-505

330 Traduisez.

1. Il a expliqué son rôle de manière inattendue.
2. Elle a bien chanté son air.
3. Ils ont répondu avec colère.
4. Si tu as déjà vu le film, on peut en voir un autre.
5. C'est joliment dit.
6. Il se mit à pleuvoir soudainement.
7. J'irai bientôt la voir à Glasgow.
8. Il s'est finalement éteint à l'âge de 92 ans.
9. Si tu vas en haut, n'oublie pas d'éteindre la lumière.
10. Quand avez-vous parlé à la victime pour la dernière fois ?

331 Utilisez *still* ou *yet*.

1. Do you … love me?
2. Have you talked to the boss …?
3. I … believe that he lied to us.
4. He hasn't said anything …
5. They … won't admit it.
6. I haven't written that letter …

332 Traduisez en employant *yet* ou *still*.

1. Il n'a pas encore acheté sa nouvelle voiture.
2. Le bébé ne parle toujours pas.
3. Je crois qu'ils sont encore au lit.
4. Jonathan n'a pas encore terminé son travail.
5. L'accusé *(defendant)* n'a pas encore parlé.
6. L'accusé ne parle toujours pas.

333 Mettez l'adverbe de fréquence à la place qui convient.

1. One or two of the club women had called on her. (only)
2. Mrs Briggs believed in keeping her distance, too. (always)
3. Has she been to Denmark? (ever)
4. They are not ready on time. (often)
5. On Sunday evenings she went to a lecture on philosophy. (sometimes)
6. You can just tell *(ici : savoir)* when he is happy. (never)
7. He had seen Mrs Briggs so generous before. (never)
8. It's the worst concert I've heard. (ever)
9. It doesn't rain here. (often)
10. "Have you met any of my cousins?" "No, I have." (never)

Adverbes de degré   § 506-514

334 Traduisez.

1. C'est un peu mieux.
2. Je crois qu'Ives est un peu soûl.
3. Ça leur a beaucoup plu.
4. Cet endroit est tellement mieux maintenant.
5. Tiens, il a neigé un petit peu.
6. Je leur ai à peine parlé.
7. Presque 80 000 personnes ont assisté à ce concert.
8. Je ne suis pas assez riche pour pouvoir me payer cet hôtel.
9. Je n'ai pas vraiment faim. Je n'ai vraiment pas faim.
10. Elle avait presque envie de démissionner.

335 Traduisez.

1. Malheureusement, je suis loin d'avoir fini.
2. J'ai compté à peine vingt personnes.
3. Mon petit frère sait à peine parler, encore moins *(let alone)* écrire.
4. Il a fait encore plus chaud que l'année dernière.
5. C'est plutôt un pays riche.
6. Ils sont assez paresseux.
7. Je ne veux même pas lui parler au téléphone.
8. Même Kevin ne serait pas d'accord avec toi.

336 *So* et *too*. Traduisez.

1. Ne marche pas si vite.
2. Ce livre est beaucoup trop difficile à lire.
3. Il mange tellement. Il mange trop.
4. C'est un voisin beaucoup trop dangereux.
5. Il a tellement mangé qu'il en a été malade.
6. J'ai trop à faire ; je suis débordée *(overworked)*.
7. C'est trop. Je ne pourrai pas tout manger.
8. C'est si propre qu'on ne veut plus s'en servir.

Adverbes d'ajout, de liaison, de modalité § 515-521

337 Adverbes d'ajout. Traduisez.

1. Ils parlent aussi l'allemand et l'italien.
2. Que pouvions-nous faire d'autre ?
3. Moi aussi, je veux être musicien.
4. Nous avons aussi des ordinateurs portables, si vous voulez.
5. Autre chose pour vous, Madame ?
6. De plus, il ne nous est pas permis de les vendre.
7. Non seulement elle joue bien, mais elle compose aussi de la musique.
8. Mon réveil n'a pas sonné. De plus, j'ai eu du mal à faire démarrer ma voiture.

338 Adverbes de liaison. Traduisez.

1. Tom felt ill, but went to work all the same. However, he didn't manage to concentrate.
2. I've never liked Harry and yet I've decided to help him.
3. I know you don't like having guests around. Still, you could make an effort.
4. Stop cheating, otherwise I'll report you.
5. Actually, I can't talk to you right now. I'll call you back.
6. "Don't worry, we'll manage somehow." "I somehow doubt it."
7. These figures don't prove anything. And besides, who worked them out?
8. We have more and more customers and therefore we need more workers.
9. She is the eldest daughter and thus heir to the title.
10. It's not very useful. It's beautiful, though, don't you think?

339 Adverbes de modalité. Retrouvez l'équivalent anglais des mots ou expressions suivants.

1. probablement
2. franchement
3. on pourrait dire que…
4. assurément
5. peut-être
6. heureusement
7. sans aucun doute
8. à mon avis
9. on espère que…
10. sûrement
11. bien sûr
12. il faut le reconnaître
13. manifestement
14. il est surprenant que…
15. certainement
16. de toute évidence
17. vraisemblablement
18. naturellement

Les mots dérivés § 526-532

340 Soulignez les préfixes dans les mots suivants.
Puis traduisez chaque mot.

counter-clockwise • asymmetry • incoherence • re-evaluate • forearm •
disconnected • undo • irreproachable • mistrust • amoral • foreground •
illegal • forecast • rebuild • misspell • undoubtedly • immature •
non-smoker • ex-husband

341 Décomposez les mots suivants en précisant la nature de chaque élément.
Puis traduisez.

EXEMPLES : *stewardess* : nom formé d'un nom *(steward)* et du suffixe du
féminin *(-ess)* : <u>hôtesse de l'air</u> – *happiness* : nom formé d'un adjectif
(happy) et d'un suffixe exprimant un état *(-ness)* : <u>bonheur</u>

waitress • boyhood • stardom • useful • sadden • driver • hairy •
refusal • friendliness • catastrophic • childless • foolish • laughable •
strangely • violinist • Catholicism • backwards • childlike • popularize •
symbolical

La composition § 534

342 Décomposez les mots suivants, en précisant la nature de chaque élément.
Puis traduisez.

underpaid • undercooked • outrun • overeat • overdressed • upgrade •
outgrow • uplifting • overreact • overlap • underrate • overrate •
outdistance • upstage

343 Commentez l'expression *out-Herod Herod* qui signifie « être très violent »,
« en rajouter ».

Corrigés

Le groupe verbal

1 Les verbes à particules et les verbes prépositionnels

1 1. He has not answered my letter yet.
2. He is looking for his keys.
3. He lacks courage.
4. Yesterday, we waited for a taxi for 20 minutes.
5. Have you phoned Judith?
6. What do you think of that?
7. I've thought about what you said.
8. She remembers him.
9. Do you trust him (her)?

2 1. She plays the violin beautifully.
2. What are you staring at?
3. He entered the room without knocking.
4. You have not dealt with the subject.
5. Do you need a dictionary?
6. I have enough money to pay for the meal.
7. We will discuss this matter later on.

3 1. go away 2. took off 3. take (your passport) along 4. get (my money) back 5. put on 6. eat out 7. move along 8. do (the kitchen) over 9. given up 10. come around (*ou* round)

4 1. call in (*s'arrêter à*) 2. called off (*annuler*) 3. carry on (*continuer*) 4. cut down (*réduire*) 5. ended up (*finir par*) 6. getting along (*ou* on) (*s'entendre avec*) 7. hang around (*traîner*) 8. put off (*remettre à plus tard*) 9. running out (*manquer*) 10. turn (me) on (*"brancher", plaire à*)

5 1. broken out 2. carried out 3. got about 4. got through 5. turned down 6. burst in 7. worn off 8. turned out

2 Les verbes *be, have, do*

6 1. That is/he has 2. He has had/at Paul's/it is 3. It has 4. she is 5. What is/she is 6. He has. 7. He is

7 1. Did you have 2. she has not got (*ou* hasn't got/does not have/doesn't have) 3. I have never had 4. they had 5. Have you really got (*ou* Do you really have)/I have

got to (*ou* have to) 6. I do not usually have 7. we did not have to 8. I have had 9. we did not have 10. we have got (*ou* we have)/we do not have

8 1. He will be fourteen in December.
2. You ought to be ashamed.
3. He has (got) blue eyes.
4. Are you hungry or thirsty?
5. We had a lot of visitors last summer.
6. Will you have some more?
7. Did you have a good time?
8. They are the same age.
9. I've got (*ou* have) everything I need.
10. How tall (*ou* high) is it?

9 1. I've done it for years 2. There is – there are 3. they had not seen each other for years 4. It has been a long time since 5. Twenty years ago tonight 6. There were – there were 7. 52 years ago 8. a hundred years

1. Je ne suis pas une débutante ; il y a des années que je le fais. 2. Gagner est un mot important. Il y a un individu qui arrive à faire ce qu'il voulait et il y en a des centaines de milliers qui échouent. 3. À présent, ils avaient vingt ans et il y avait des années qu'ils ne s'étaient pas vus. 4. Il y a longtemps que tu n'es pas venu en ville. 5. Il y a vingt ans ce soir, je dînais ici avec mon ami. 6. L'immeuble grouillait de chats. Il y avait même quelques chiens… Il y a eu beaucoup de plaintes. 7. Il y a 52 ans, j'ai trouvé un sac plein d'argent. J'ai pris ce sac et je m'en suis servi pour gagner plus d'argent. 8. Il n'y a que cent ans que cette école existe.

10 1. There is an Indian restaurant in my street. I had dinner there three days ago.
2. "When did you last see your mother?" "Almost two years ago."
3. He has been an M.P. for 28 years.
4. "How long is it (*ou* has it been) since you last visited London?" (*ou* "When did you last visit London?") "Five or six years."
5. It is 9,000 km from Paris to San Francisco.
6. I have known him for eight years.
7. How far is it to the next bus stop?
8. Twenty years ago it was different.

11 1. I guess I did 2. don't you – I do 3. we did 4. you did, did you 5. didn't you 6. please do 7. do you 8. didn't you 9. did you 10. I really don't

12 1. I told you, didn't I? (*ou* I did tell you, didn't I?)
2. You don't know the man, I do.
3. "I could get a better job." "I doubt that." "You do? Why?"
4. "He lives here now." "Does he? I didn't know that."
5. "He told me something about you." "He did? What was that?"
6. I do not understand why he came so early. Do *you*?
7. "I told you to use the computer." "That's what I did."
8. We know where it is. Do *you*?

3 Le présent

13 runs • works • pays • lies • cries • catches • laughs • goes • hurries • passes • relaxes

14 1. What time does she get up? 2. Is it raining (very hard)? 3. What are you reading? 4. Does she agree (with me)? 5. Do you like sweets? 6. When is he coming back? 7. When does she leave home every day? 8. What do they do? 9. Does she know him? 10. What are you waiting for?

15 1. am I dreaming? 2. dream – love 3. is having 4. look – are you thinking 5. Are you writing – I always write 6. is coming – do you want 7. is coming up, thinks 8. say – frightens – are not being 9. don't have – we do – do they – are you talking about – have – you're coming – are not trekking 10. look – are you looking for – I'm not actually looking for – I'm passing through

16 présent simple
• énoncer une caractéristique :
1. weighs 2. is 8. am sorry
• relater des actions successives :
4. begin 7. ties – rises – yawns – begins – stops – looks down – shakes…

• décrire une habitude :
3. do you shop 11. say – say
• décrire une scène à la manière d'une indication scénique :
6. he sits
• avec un verbe peu compatible avec be + V-*ing* :
5. don't like 6. reckon 8. doesn't matter 10. don't care, doesn't bother – don't know

présent en *be* + V-*ing*
• décrire une action en cours de déroulement :
4. is falling – is dropping 5. are you asking 6. he's thinking – I'm thinking 11. you're all being
• exprimer un point de vue dépréciatif :
8. I'm always doing 11. You're always saying
• annoncer la réalisation d'une action déjà envisagée :
2. I am just going 9. is speaking.

17 1. I'm not cooking today.
2. I'm thinking about moving to London.
3. What I'm trying to say is that you can't come back here.
4. If I don't do it now, it won't be ready tonight.
5. You both need a break. Why don't you go away?
6. I thought I'd better tell you: I'm going away. I feel like a change.
7. "Does your mother agree?" "Yes, she does."
8. "This is Patrick. How are you?" "Patrick!" "I hope I'm not disturbing you."
9. "He'll be looked after, don't worry." "Are you telling me he's not well?"
10. Every night he tells the kids a story and then goes to bed.

4 Le prétérit

18 1. I saw 2. Did you fly 3. She taught 4. She did not think 5. I thought 6. He lost 7. I sent 8. Why did you send 9. He did not sleep 10. He laid 11. Why did you lie 12. He lay 13. He fell 14. She felt 15. He brought 16. did they buy 17. It meant 18. She led.

19 1. À 18 ans, j'ai décidé d'étudier la médecine.
2. Que devrais-je dire si l'on me demandait quand je l'ai vu pour la dernière fois ?
3. Il lui parla (parlait) comme si c'était un bébé.
4. Que se passerait-il si j'y allais ?
5. Elle arrêta de travailler de bonne heure, dit qu'elle avait mal à la tête, fit sa valise et prit la route.
6. Le mieux serait que tu en discutes avec elle.
7. J'aimerais beaucoup mieux que tu ne lui racontes pas.
8. Si seulement j'avais leur âge tout en sachant ce que je sais maintenant.
9. Assis à côté d'elle, Adam secoua la tête. Il était grand, brun. Elle pensa qu'il ressemblait à l'un de ces hommes parfaits des publicités de magazine.

20 1. I was thinking 2. were enjoying – was 3. Beck did not know what she was talking about – she persisted – he ran off – was annoying 4. I was asking 5. happened – was going – had – was following – turned around – never saw 6. were you doing *ou* did you do (What were you doing? *Que faisais-tu ?* What did you do? *Qu'as-tu fait ?*) – came in.

21 *Mr James S.* **killed** *his wife in a dream last night. He* **dreamed** *(ou dreamt) that his daughter who* **was sleeping** *in the same room* **was being attacked** *by assassins and he* **fired** *on them, with the result that he* **killed** *his wife.*

Yesterday Mr S., his wife and their two daughters **went** to bed as usual about 10. Towards midnight Mr S. **thought** he **heard** the window open. Turning over, he **saw** two masked men enter the room with knives. One **went** and **stood** over the daughter. In frantic terror Mr S. **fired** the pistol which he **was clutching** in his hand beneath the pillow. Switching on the light he **saw** that blood **was trickling** from his wife's head. He then **realized** he had been dreaming but his wife **was** dead.

22 1. She was 28 and she was going to conquer the world.
2. She didn't know what they were looking for.
3. He asked if she knew who the keys belonged to.
4. He didn't only want to please her.
5. The children were not listening, they were too busy watching the match.
6. Every evening after work he would go (ou he used to go) and see her (ou he went to see her); he would tell her about his day at work; she would pretend that she was listening.
7. It was a lovely morning. She looked around: the dew was shining on the grass, the birds were singing.
8. When the waves were breaking, Jimmy was always at the beach. He liked to surf.

5 Le *present perfect*

23 1. have you been 2. She has caught 3. I haven't heard 4. He has forgotten 5. They have just gone 6. She has spent 7. Have you spoken 8. Have you thought 9. She has wept 10. We haven't paid

24 1. I have been reading 2. Have you been smoking? 3. They have been fishing 4. We have been waiting 5. have they been looking 6. have you been doing? 7. He has been sleeping 8. have you been wearing 9. I have been shopping 10. I have been asking

25 1. *(for)* Je le connais depuis huit ans.
2. *(for)* Il a voyagé pendant six mois en Australie.
3. *(since)* Cela fait longtemps qu'il a joué cette sonate.
4. *(since)* Sont-ils vraiment ici depuis lundi ?
5. *(since)* Je ne les ai pas vus depuis la naissance de leur fils.
6. *(for)* Est-ce que je peux laisser ça ici pendant quelques heures ?
7. *(since)* Depuis quand regardes-tu la télévision ?
8. *(for)* Elle est mariée depuis deux ans.
9. *(since)* Ça fait vingt ans qu'elle est morte.
10. *(for)* Je l'aimerai toujours.

26 1. I have been stuck [...] for seven years
2. He has been known [...] since a teenager
3. [...] who's been doing this for a while.
4. It had been raining for ten days 5. Since
2000 [...] has won 6. has tripled since 1991
7. had been wandering [...] for nearly an
hour 8. has happened [...] since he turned
9. Since July 1st [...] have been having (*ou*
have had).

27 1. He has been awake for three hours.
2. He has been awake since three (in the
afternoon).
3. He has been at sea for more than six
weeks.
4. She has been a professor of economics at
Oxford since 2004.
5. We haven't been paid for (*ou* in) five
weeks.
6. "How long have you been doing this?"
"Since I left university, nine years ago."
7. A whole year has passed since they came
back.
8. I've been trying to open this door for 45
(forty-five) minutes.
9. Her (*ou* His) novel has been a bestseller
for nearly a year.
10. The garden had been neglected for years
when we bought it.

28 1. You've been phoning for ages. Haven't
you nearly finished?
2. "You look exhausted." "Yes, I've been jogging and I've not run for (*ou* in) years."
3. What have you been doing? I've been
waiting for you for hours.
4. Have you already done your homework?
I've been working for hours and I've not
finished yet.

29 1. He has been sleeping 2. He has slept
3. I have ever slept 4. I have taught – have
never met 5. I have been teaching (*ou* I have
taught) 6. Have you smoked 7. Have you
been smoking? 8. He has painted 9. she has
been painting 10. He has drunk

30 1. What have you been doing 2. I have
not laughed 3. I have been trying – I have
hardly said 4. I have never seen (*américain* :
I never saw) – hasn't happened 5. have been

found – have been making – have been
making – has been growing

31 1. He had never seen 2. she moved – she
had planned 3. she had gone 4. they talked –
they had visited – never seemed 5. she had
cried – she began 6. she behaved – had
changed 7. he had forgotten 8. she was –
Had he forgotten? 9. She took – she had
expected

32 1. A Chicago judge today **granted**
divorce to Mr R. on the grounds of his wife's
silence. The plaintiff **informed** the Court
that, although his wife **had lived** in his
house, she **had not spoken** to him for
eighteen years. He **declared** that it **was**
like living with a ghost. He **had consulted**
physicians in the effort to get her to talk
but it **was** impossible to surprise her into
uttering a word.

2. Through the arrest of three former prisoners of the San Quentin prison in California
who **had been released** on parole at various
times last year, it **became** known today that
counterfeit $ 10 bank notes, with which they
had been supplied were manufactured
on the prison's own printing presses. In
examining the men's prison records, the
Secret Service **found** that all three **had had**
access to the printing shop while they were
serving their terms.

3. I **went** back to Oxford recently. I **had not
been** back since we all **left**, almost twenty
years ago. I **was surprised** to see how little
the city **had changed**. Although there **were**
new buildings everywhere and the main
crossroads **had been widened**, the main
landmarks **remained** in place.

33 1. I had gone – there was – I passed – she
was smiling – there was – I stood – came
2. stopped – stared – needed – had needed
3. she was standing – he began – she hadn't
had time

4. she looked – sniffed – it was – she had missed (*ou* had been missing) – she had thought of – had been (*ou* was)

5. cheated – crash-landed – had been filming (*ou* had filmed) – had

34 1. She **pushed** open the door. Women **were sitting** at the table. She **saw** her mother among them. In five years her hair **had gone** grey and she **looked** very old. Everyone **stopped** what they **were doing.**

2. "What **happened**?" "A massive heart attack. He'**d had** two or three warnings before but…" […] She **touched** her chest. "And he'**d been having** these pains in the upper arm. I **told** him to take his tablets. And off he **went** to open the bar. The next time I **saw** him he **was** dead."

7 Les formes verbales : synthèse

35 1. "I **am going** out. **Do you want** anything?" 2. "Pleased to meet you, Sandy. Where **do** you **come** from?" "**I come** from Maryville. "How long **have you been** here?" "I've just only arrived." 3. **Does he know** what we **are talking about**? 4. What **are you four plotting**? 5. The bus **leaves** at half past ten. 6. "Your report is a disgrace." "It's not fair. **I'm trying hard** (*ou* **I've been trying hard**), really." 7. He **has been running** this restaurant for more than twenty years. 8. It's the first time she **has kissed** him. 9. "Wake up! It's the day **I've been waiting for**. Come on, get up!" "What is it? **I'm sleeping!**" 10. The jeans market **is shrinking**. Jeans sales **have slumped** by more than three million pairs in the year to May. Yet, denim **remains** fashionable – as long as it's used for anything but jeans. Whether **it is** hip or nostalgic its appeal is universal.

36 1. What happens when the doors are shut?

2. What's all this noise ? What's happening?

3. "Did you hear the phone?" "Yes, I'm coming."

4. I have used this pen for years.

5. He bought his ticket this morning: he's flying to London this afternoon.

6. It's the first time I have been away from her.

7. You're always sleeping!

8. How long has he been sitting here?

9. This is a problem that has been creeping up on us for years.

10. Have you been working all that time?

37 1. What about last night, did you sleep at all?

2. You didn't listen to what he said.

3. We went there three years ago.

4. "How many comedies did Shakespeare write?" "I don't know, but I've read them all."

5. I've been walking too fast, that's why I'm tired.

6. You're shaking. How many coffees have you had?

7. You never came back home once in five years.

8. "Why did you accept?" "I couldn't say no."

9. What have you done to this knife? The blade is twisted.

10. "We were just about to start without you." "Sorry, I got lost."

38 1. works 2. worked 3. has been working 4. has worked (*ou* has been working) 5. is working 6. does not work 7. did not work 8. has never worked

9. has written 10. wrote 11. has been writing 12. writes

39 verbes au prétérit

She once said… : *once* implique que la déclaration appartient au passé.

She was born in Illinois in 1935… : le fait est révolu.

she attended the University of Ottawa… : fait révolu, elle n'est plus étudiante.

… settled in Canada in 1957… : fait révolu.

I always wanted… : volonté située dans le passé ; maintenant, elle est bien écrivain.

it seemed impossible… : impression passée, coupée du présent

She was awarded… : fait appartenant au passé.

was published in 1993 : fait révolu

I wanted : fait révolu
Before they were : *before* implique un fait révolu, coupé du présent.

verbes au *present perfect*
Has become : bilan dans le présent.
She has lived there since that date : action commencée dans le passé qui continue dans le présent (rôle de *since that date*); traduction en français : « elle y habite ».
I have written : bilan dans le présent.
has written : c'est le résultat présent qui importe.
has always meant : action commencée dans le passé qui continue dans le présent (rôle de *always* : toujours, y compris au moment présent).
This change has had : bilan dans le présent.
they have had : bilan dans le présent.

40 1. Have you tasted 2. invented – mixed – taught – has become 3. has been electrocuted – was found – touched – was electrocuted 4. happened – met – swapped – I have not heard – she has not heard 5. gave – has stepped 6. has been 7. said – 've made 8. have never had (*américain* : I never had) – saw

41 1. changed – lost – slid 2. has created – became – told 3. have completed – have come – belonged – abandoned – was enveloped

42 1. taught – met – fell 2. read 3. have known 4. thought – had forgotten 5. laid – left 6. have never ridden 7. lay down 8. fell – broke 9. have you run 10. has caught

43 1. lose 2. understood 3. choose 4. rung 5. brought 6. didn't think 7. set (*ou* began) 8. does the sun rise? 9. found 10. wrote this letter

44 1. someone tells – the world is going – I simply don't believe 2. have you had – do you have – I have never done – I have kept – I have done 3. you did not live – I brought – I came 4. was not becoming 5. we are having – don't you come

45 1. do you know – I have been saying – do you understand 2. I have told you – you were not paying 3. she died 4. I saw – he had been fighting 5. I had known 6. have been saying – it has certainly been true 7. they picked up – he was carrying – they had never seen 8. you turned – (you) went – I haven't finished – you haven't been working – you have been reading – you have been doing 9. I had been staying 10. he was going

8 Le passif

46 1. start – do not finish 2. are offered 3. is taken

4. are being neglected – is pressing – are being overlooked – are opting

5. was built – was remodeled – was partially destroyed – was acquired – operated – it was sold 6. occurred – were killed – were carried – were buried

7. have spent 8. has been recorded 9. has largely replaced 10. it has often been said – have been written 11. has not changed

12. will be found 13. will come 14. may be easier said than done 15. may well not close 16. we will send – will be sent – must be placed 17. will give – can be included 18. can the suburbs be blamed 19. can we make 20. be taught

47 1. The concert was sponsored... was being transmitted... *Le concert était parrainé... était retransmis en direct...*
2. according to how much attention is paid to them. ... *selon l'attention qu'on leur prête.*
3. children... are cared for... I was asked... *on s'occupe des enfants... on m'a demandé...*
4. are spread all over the island. ...*partout sur l'île se trouvent... (*ou *il y a..., on trouve...).*
5. The washing must be done. *Il faut que la lessive soit faite.*
6. is seldom used... *s'emploie rarement...*
7. are collected... are to be sold... *sont récoltés... se vendront... (*ou *sont destinés à la vente).*
8. lots of things to be done. ... *beaucoup à faire.*

9. *Attention !* was born *n'est pas un passif.* She was born *se traduit par « Elle est née... »,* surtout pas par « Elle était née... »

10. need to be played with and talked to. ... *ont besoin qu'on joue avec eux et qu'on leur parle.*

48 1. Our programme will be watched by millions of viewers. 2. They must be made acceptable. 3. The Admiral's Cup was instituted in 1957 by the Royal Ocean Racing Club. 4. ... but he was obeyed by everyone. 5. ... most of the tea was being brought back by steamers. 6. He had been told about them by his father. 7. Those who arrive first will be greeted by the president. 8. Several experiments in that field have been carried out by scientists... 9. In the modern world, magic has been replaced by technology. 10. Who was it written by?

49 1. I am told there will be... 2. *Transposition peu souhaitable.* 3. The park gates will be opened... They are usually locked... 4. *Transposition peu souhaitable.* 5. Goods were regularly being stolen... *Pour* he set a trap, *transposition peu souhaitable.* 6. *Transposition peu souhaitable.* 7. The news of the strike had been announced... 8. *Transposition peu souhaitable.* 9. If every house was painted... the balance of nature would seriously be disturbed.

50 1. People under 16 are not admitted.
2. Yes, it was built in 1880.
3. The plane was delayed.
4. He ought to be locked up.
5. He is sure he can solve the problem.
6. I do not agree.
7. She was not offered the job. (*ou* She hasn't been offered the job.)
8. His colleagues gave him a TV set when he retired.
9. Yes, he was an English painter who was recognized as a revolutionary genius, made his name with painting seascapes and has left some three hundred paintings.

51 1. Education is acknowledged to be...
2. Frank Lloyd Wright is considered to have been... 3. Chicago is known to be... 4. The

man... is understood to have been... 5. He was later reported to be dismayed (*ou* to have been dismayed)... 6. She is believed to have paid... 7. The couple are (*ou* is) believed to have suffered... 8. This gold nugget is expected to fetch...

52 1. ethnic minorities are still discriminated against. 2. They are not properly looked after. 3. A visa has to be applied for... 4. he was shouted down... 5. the conflict has been put an end to. 6. "It is being looked into..." 7. She was lost sight of... 8. are disapproved of... 9. can only be guessed at. 10. are often referred to...

9   Le renvoi à l'avenir et le conditionel

53 1. will occur. 2. is going to come – will find out 3. Is he coming? 4. is staying 5. 'll keep 6. I'll probably see 7. 'll sell – will buy 8. are going to be

54 1. We will know tonight. *[simple prédiction]*
2. He's leaving in a few days. *[projet personnel]*
3. It's easy, I'll show you. *[décision prise sur-le-champ]*
4. "What would you like to drink?" "I'll have tea." *[décision prise sur-le-champ]*
5. I'll believe it when I see it. *[simple prédiction]*
6. "Can you come on Sunday?" "I'm afraid I can't. I'm going to the theatre." *[projet]*
7. He's not going to retire now, he's got too much to do. *[intention]*
8. Well, I'll tell you what we are going to do (*ou* what we'll do). *[décision prise sur-le-champ]*
9. The show is about to start. *[événement imminent]*
10. I'm not going to watch the match, I've got work. *[intention]*

55 1. will have seen 2. it will reach 3. they'll be discussing 4. will you be moving out 5. you'll be wanting (*ou* you will want) 6. you will have left 7. you will be spending (*ou* you will spend) 8. will look 9. will have lost

1. What would you do 2. I wouldn't worry
3. What would he have told 4. They would be
glad 5. that wouldn't be 6. she might have
succeeded 7. I could do 8. I would not accept
9. I should imagine (*ou* have imagined)
10. she couldn't live

10 Les modaux

57 très certain
(*'ll*) 6. Le téléphone sonna. "C'est sans doute
pour moi !" dit-il.

très probable
(*must*) 2. Il devait y avoir quelqu'un d'autre
(qu'eux) pour conduire la voiture.
(*must*) 8. Il doit y avoir de meilleures chan-
sons (à chanter) que celle-ci.
(*should*) 10. Elle devrait être de retour dans
quelques minutes.

possible
(*may*) 4. Il se peut qu'elle ait été responsable
de l'accident.

incertain
(*might*) 1. Ça pourrait être une bonne idée.
(*might*) 3. J'ai pensé que vous aimeriez peut-
être voir les enfants avant qu'ils n'aillent se
coucher.
(*might*) 7. Il se pourrait qu'il devienne célè-
bre un jour.

imaginable
(*could*) 5. Il se pourrait bien qu'il gagne un
millier de dollars.

difficilement imaginable
(*couldn't*) 11. Ça ne pourrait pas arriver de
nouveau.

impossible
(*can't*) 9. Ce n'est pas possible qu'il soit
mort !

58 must
1. a) You must be joking.
   b) He must have been lying.

may
2. a) You may be surprised.
   b) He may have given her a diamond
   ring.

might
3. a) We might never see each other again.
   b) She might be waiting for us at the
   airport.

can/can't
4. a) She can't be as old as…
   b) She can't be sleeping…
   c) I can't have lost his address.

should
5. a) He should speak English fluently …
   b) They should have arrived now.

59 1. She might become a vet. 2. There must
be another solution. 3. "You think he could
be gone a month?" "He might." 4. She may
not like this idea. 5. He must be three or four
years younger than her. 6. That must have
happened just before the war. 7. It could be
very embarrassing if people saw us together.
8. One might have thought he was drunk.
9. Why have you thrown (*ou* did you throw)
these clothes away? Somebody might have
wanted them.

60 1. (*could*) J'aimerais pouvoir rester ici
pour toujours.
2. (*would*) Je peux t'expliquer si seulement
tu voulais m'écouter.
3. (*can*) Interflora a lancé un site Internet
qui vous donne la possibilité d'envoyer des
fleurs de votre travail sans même décrocher
le téléphone.
4. (*will*) Cette chemise blanche classique est
indémodable.
5. (*can*) Ici, vous pouvez tout acheter, des
huîtres aux cigares !
6. (*will – can*) Les ours sont essentiellement
végétariens mais ils mangent toute viande
qu'ils peuvent attraper ou trouver.
7. (*can't*) Ce que je ne peux pas supporter,
c'est l'idée qu'il n'a cessé de mentir pendant
toutes ces années.
8. (*will*) Tu veux bien me rendre un service ?
9. (*would*) James Dean était son héros à ce
moment-là. Elle gardait toutes les photos
des magazines et les accrochait aux murs
de sa chambre.
10. (*will*) Viens avec moi, tu veux bien ?

61 1. *(can't)* « Je ne me souviens pas de l'adresse. – Tu ne te souviens même pas du nom de la rue ? »

2. *(would)* « Il dit que tu es stupide de prendre un tel risque. – C'est bien de lui ! Il a toujours quelque chose à me reprocher. »

3. *(couldn't – can't)* Lorsque j'étais enfant, je ne comprenais pas les adultes et maintenant que je suis adulte, je ne comprends pas les enfants.

4. *(would)* Ils voudraient nous faire croire que la situation s'améliore mais le fait est qu'elle empire.

5. *(would)* Aurais-tu la gentillesse de bien vouloir me prêter ton ordinateur portable ?

6. *(could)* Il a dit que c'était parfaitement évident à ses yeux.

7. *(could)* Si seulement il avait pu passer la nuit ici !

8. *(will)* Lorsque la voiture démarra, il dit : « Ça tient du miracle ! »

9. *(would)* J'avais un réveil réglé pour neuf heures mais, invariablement, tous les matins, je me réveillais avant.

10. *(could)* Je n'avais pas eu de leurs nouvelles du plus loin que je me souvienne, mais je savais qu'ils étaient encore vivants.

62 1. I couldn't leave him. Where would I go?

2. I couldn't have left him. Where would I have gone?

3. You should talk to her (*ou* him) because you can answer her (*ou* his) questions.

4. You should have talked to her (*ou* him) because you could have answered her (*ou* his) questions.

5. She would prefer you wrote in English (*ou* you to write in English).

6. She would have preferred you wrote in English (*ou* you to write in English).

7. Surely things could improve, life could be better.

8. Surely things could have improved, life could have been better.

9. You would have nothing to lose and you might have a great deal to gain.

10. You would have had nothing to lose and you might have had a great deal to gain.

63 1. You must take time. 2. She must be reading 3. he should be riding 4. we should celebrate 5. you can always tell 6. they can't be having 7. She could be playing 8. I couldn't hear 9. She might be working 10. Might I suggest

64 1. you must be 2. must have been 3. must be leaving 4. may go 5. might have loved 6. might have

65 1. Couldn't it have waited 2. He could have done 3. they can't possibly be doing 4. I can't explain 5. I couldn't find it. Could I have dropped 6. You should have called me. 7. You should come 8. shouldn't have come

66 1. Who will come with us?
2. Would you do me a favour?
3. Will you call me later?
4. I wish it would work.
5. I think she won't answer that question *ou* I don't think she will answer that question.
6. I wish somebody would answer.
7. She won't go, and that's that.
8. Will you shut the door, please?
9. She wishes he wouldn't complain all the time.
10. She wouldn't let him pay.

67 contraindre, donner un ordre
(must) 1. La file de gauche doit tourner à gauche. [fréquent]

interdire
(must not) 8. Tu ne dois pas mentir. [fréquent]
(shalt not) 11. Tu ne voleras point. [rare]

offrir, suggérer de
(shall) 7. Désirez-vous que je vous débarrasse de cette assiette ? [fréquent]
(might) 15. Tu pourrais aborder la question avec lui. [moins fréquent]

donner un conseil
(should) 4. Je pense que tu devrais voir un médecin. [fréquent]
(shouldn't) 5. Il n'aurait pas dû t'en parler. [fréquent]

accorder une permission

(can) 10. Vous pouvez partir tous les deux. Je n'ai pas besoin de vous. [fréquent]

(may) 13. Chaque électeur n'a le droit de voter que pour un seul candidat. [moins fréquent]

demander une permission

(can) 2. Est-ce que je peux laisser mes affaires ici ? [fréquent]

(could) 3. Pourrais-je vous parler, Monsieur ? [fréquent]

(may) 6. Puis-je te rappeler que tout ceci est fait en ta faveur ? [fréquent]

(might) 12. Pourrais-je vous parler un instant ? [moins fréquent]

refuser une permission

(can't) 9. Si vous avez moins de 17 ans, vous ne pouvez pas conduire une voiture en Grande-Bretagne. [fréquent]

(may not) 14. Deux lignes blanches parallèles signifient que vous n'avez pas le droit de doubler. [moins fréquent]

68 1. I'm hungry. Can I have a snack ?
2. You must obey the law.
3. You can borrow my paper if you like.
4. May I see your passport, please?
5. Shall I help you (*ou* give you a hand)?
6. You shouldn't have drunk so much.
7. They should be in bed, not watching television.
8. Visitors must not feed the animals.
9. Might I give you some advice?
10. Could I use your telephone?
11. You should have told me!
12. You must not touch (it).

69 1. It is strange that he shouldn't be here.
2. In case he should ask, tell him I'll be back on Wednesday.
3. What do you suggest I should take (*ou* I take)?
4. It is funny that you should say that.
5. It is important that you should listen carefully.
6. They insisted that we should have dinner with them.
7. If you should change your mind, please let me know. (*ou* Should you change …)

8. It is absurd that she should be paid less than him.
9. I gave her a map lest (*ou* for fear that) she should get lost.
10. He suggested that she should sell her car.

70 1. would have thought 2. should I get 3. would you like 4. should change – should you change 5. should be 6. should have happened 7. would stop 8. should be 9. would be 10. wouldn't start

71 1. Que devrais-je dire ? (*ou* Quoi dire ?) Comment vais-je formuler cela ?
2. Ma vie était finie et rien ne serait plus comme avant.
3. Lorsque je lui demandais pourquoi elle avait épousé Bob, elle disait qu'elle n'avait pas eu le choix.
4. Elle disait souvent qu'il fallait profiter le plus possible de ce que nous avions.
5. Il y avait cinq chambres, et il était tout naturel que Charlie ait la plus grande.
6. Elle pourrait faire quelque chose de mieux. J'aimerais bien que tu lui parles d'aller à l'université. (*ou* Si seulement tu voulais bien lui parler…)
7. Je suppose que je pensais que ça continuerait toujours ainsi.
8. « Tu penses que c'est bien l'endroit ? — Oui, ça devrait être exactement ici. »
9. Tu veux bien m'aider à faire ça ?
10. C'était une chatte très patiente. Elle restait des heures à observer les oiseaux.

11 Autres façons d'exprimer la modalité

72 1. you can imagine 2. we could buy 3. I could (not) have answered 4. you'll be able to 5. she could keep 6. you can see 7. you were unable to 8. he could pick on – he couldn't 9. I was able to 10. she was never able to

73 1. she would – I would see 2. He used to be 3. she was now used to 4. He would throw 5. I used to feel 6. I used to play 7. he is used to spending 8. there used to be

74 1. He'd better not drive.

2. You shouldn't take any notice of what he tells you.

3. I think I'd better go. I need to be on my own.

4. "He should sleep now." "Will he be alright, do you think?" "He's just in a shock. A few hours' rest ought to take care of it."

5. I decided I had better be present when she met him.

6. I've still got the flu. I ought to be (at) home in bed.

7. You'd better think carefully about what you're going to do.

8. It's a disgrace. There ought to be a notice.

9. She was just a child. She oughtn't to have known about that kind of thing.

10. I should have taken a taxi instead of walking back home.

75 1. must be prepared 2. have to say 3. mustn't cry 4. must convince 5. don't have to do 6. mustn't let 7. have to do – has to do 8. must admit 9. have to wait 10. must tell me

76 1. have to go 2. must absolutely go 3. don't have to lie 4. have to go 5. must admit 6. don't have to go on 7. must (*ou* have to) concentrate – mustn't get 8. doesn't have to worry

77 1. You need not 2. does not need 3. They need not 4. You need not 5. I do not need to go

78 1. You need not have driven (*ou* You did not need to drive) so fast: we had plenty of time.

2. She was well: she did not need to take (*ou* she needn't have taken) more pills.

3. They need not have worried: they would succeed.

4. You need not have written to her.

5. There was plenty of food in the fridge: I did not need to go (*ou* needn't have gone) shopping.

79 1. I must say I was rather surprised.

2. He doesn't see very well: he has to wear glasses.

3. You'll have to get used to it.

4. Why do they have to obey him?

5. He was to die four years later.

6. He must have missed his train.

7. You are to do (*ou* You must do) as you are told.

8. They are to marry in two months.

9. You must be looking forward to seeing him again.

10. He must have been in England when the accident happened.

12 Le subjonctif et l'impératif

80 1. you should say that 2. I (should) stay 3. we stopped 4. this be the case 5. Come what may 6. I were you 7. (God) bless you! 8. he (should) be prepared for this 9. need be 10. as it were

81 1. Come back! 2. Let's ask him (*ou* her)! 3. Don't run! 4. Be quiet! 5. Do be careful! 6. Let's not complain! (*ou* Don't let's complain!). 7. Do as you're told. 8. Don't let them go! 9. Leave him alone. 10. Listen, will you? *[intonation descendante]*

13 Les reprises elliptiques

82 1. Oh, yes, he has. 2. No. I didn't. 3. Yes, she does. 4. Yes, I will. 5. Simon did. 6. Oh, have they? 7. No, I am not. 8. Does he? 9. I don't think so. 10. I'd love to.

83 1. You're not allowed to. 2. I'm afraid he has (*ou* I'm afraid so). 3. Yes, I expect so. 4. Of course she can. 5. I'm afraid not. 6. Oh, did she? 7. Because they told us to. (*ou* Because we were told to.) 8. I don't know how to.

84 1. So does he. 2. *They [accentué]* did not. 3. I don't. 4. So it does. 5. Neither have I. 6. No, he is not. 7. So will I (*ou* shall I). 8. Neither (*ou* Nor) have I. 9. Neither (*ou* Nor) did I. 10. So would he.

85 1. isn't she? 2. are they? 3. didn't you? 4. will they? 5. didn't they? 6. do you? 7. could they? 8. shall we? 9. wasn't there? 10. won't you?

Le groupe nominal

14 Le genre et le nombre du nom

86 woman • mother • aunt • niece • wife • lioness • cow • vixen • bitch • girl-friend • female • she-bear • actress • waitress • female cat • goddess • barmaid • mare • daughter-in law • sow

87 1. *nurse* : peut désigner un homme ou une femme.
2. *she-bear* : féminin formé autrement que par dérivation en -*ess*.
3. *ship* : traditionnellement associé au féminin.
4. *spokesman* : seul nom marqué par le masculin
5. *teacher* : seul nom indifférent au genre.

88 [z] selves • ideas • kids • members • tomatoes • ears • corporations • bachelors • systems
[s] groups • books • necks • chiefs • units
[ɪz] wishes • peaches • offices • churches

89 [z] snails • shells • gardens • numbers • borders • lawns • paths • gardeners • flowers • carnations • dahlias • vegetables • tomatoes • salads • strawberries • slugs
[s] pellets • plants • carrots • pests
[ɪz] courses • roses

90 brushes • chiefs • crossroads • photos • paths • species • ghettos • criteria • thieves • crises • loaves • brothers *ou* brethren • potatoes • media • leaves • analyses • wolves • phenomena • aircraft

91 men • children • lice • feet • oxen • mice • teeth • geese • theses • campuses

92 *grass* : pas de pluriel, indénombrable (≠ *a grass, grasses* : herbes, graminées et, en argot, mouchards) • *leaf* ▷ *leaves* : dénombrable • *staff* : pas de pluriel, collectif (≠ *staff, staves* : bâton) • *illness* ▷ *illnesses* : dénombrable • *youth* (la jeunesse) : pas de pluriel, indénombrable (≠ *a youth, youths* : un jeune, des jeunes) • *dish* ▷ *dishes* : dénombrable • *box* ▷ *boxes* : dénombrable • *porch* ▷ *porches* : dénombrable • *robbery* ▷ *robberies* : dénombrable • *business* : pas de pluriel, indénombrable (≠ *a business, businesses* : une entreprise) • *kingdom* ▷ *kingdoms* : dénombrable • *silence* : pas de pluriel hors contexte spécifique (indénombrable)

93 1. *photo* : nom abrégé; pluriel en -s et non en -es 2. *boy* : voyelle + *y* ; pluriel en -s et non -*ies* 3. *cliff* : pluriel en -s et non -*ves*. 4. *book* : seul pluriel régulier des quatre. 5. *fish* : peut prendre un -s au pluriel, contrairement aux trois autres. 6. *mouse* : pluriel irrégulier, les autres sont identiques au singulier et au pluriel. 7. *people* : le verbe qui suit est toujours au pluriel, alors que les trois autres admettent le singulier ou le pluriel, suivant le contexte. 8. *rubbish* : construction verbale au singulier, les trois autres au pluriel. 9. *news* : le verbe qui suit est toujours au singulier, les trois autres admettent le singulier et le pluriel.

94 a blade of grass • a compass *(une boussole)* – a pair of compasses *(un compas)* • a stroke of luck • a head of cattle • a slice of toast • a flash of lightning • a crash of thunder • a pair of jeans • a lump of sugar • a flake of snow

95 1. deux pièces d'un penny – un coût de deux pence 2. des espèces de fruits différentes – des fruits 3. des flèches, des fléchettes – le jeu de fléchettes 4. des courants d'air – le jeu de dames 5. les coutumes – la douane 6. deux boussoles – deux compas

96 verbe au singulier
athletics, news

verbe au pluriel
glasses, savings, clothes, outskirts, shorts, spectacles, remains,

admettent les deux accords
barracks, headquarters, politics

97 1. have 2. is 3. were 4. lives (*ou* live) – is (*ou* are) 5. do 6. has 7. think – is 8. is – have

> Les expressions *a number of, the majority of, a couple of, a group of* et *a lot of, the rest of* + nom pluriel ou pronom, sont généralement suivies d'un verbe au pluriel.

98 1. Mathematics has 2. The salmon swim 3. The cattle are 4. My family gather (*ou* gathers) 5. The crew is (*ou* are) 6. police were 7. This news is

99 verbe au singulier

Cyprus • Honduras • the Netherlands • Wales • the United States of America

verbe au pluriel

the Bahamas • the Philippines • the Maldives • the West Indies *(les Antilles)*

> *Ceux qui admettent un verbe au pluriel désignent des archipels aux îles bien distinctes.*

100 sons-in-law • goods-trains • menservants *(valets de chambre)* • tooth-brushes • woman-haters • passers-by • grown-ups • sit-ins • step-fathers

101 1. Try not to forget your luggage at the airport!
2. You should follow my advice.
3. I can't find my trousers (*ou* US : pants).
4. I have bought new furniture for my flat.
5. Kicking John was the best goalkeeper in the world cup.

102 1. The headquarters of the political parties are protected by the police.
2. The public have (*ou* has) not been told the latest news yet.
3. The barracks were (*ou* was) destroyed by the army.
4. The audience were (*ou* was) so satisfied that they applauded the actors in the middle of the play.
5. Ten police were wounded during the riots.
6. All luggage is examined at the customs.
7. All my family have fair hair and blue eyes.
8. The American government has decided to increase its fight against terrorism.
9. I haven't found a better means to do it.
10. Two aircraft have crashed after take-off.

15 Les déterminants du nom

103 1. Men and women are (*ou* Man and woman are) supposed to be equal.
2. Courage, love and generosity are rare values.
3. Speed can kill, drugs too.
4. If you pour too much oil in the saucepan, it may catch fire (*ou* burn).
5. I'll have to go there by car or by plane since train drivers are on strike.

104 1. The hospital is between the school and the church: I remember going to school and to church here, but not to (the) hospital.
2. I like books, even if I don't read them.
3. What did you have for breakfast?
4. Blue and orange are my favourite (US : favorite) colours.
5. Everybody should speak English nowadays.

105 1. Diseases like cancer, AIDS, hepatitis may one day be bad memories.
2. Days are much shorter in winter than in spring.
3. I had to stay fourteen days (*ou* two weeks *ou* a fortnight) in bed owing to a bad cold.
4. I am fed up with television.
5. I don't know anyone living in North America or Australia.

106-107 valeur de généralité

Les miroirs : Ø mirrors • *des glaces* : Ø panes – ice-creams • *le style* : Ø style • *des choses compliquées* : Ø complicated things • *des statues* : Ø statues • *l'enfance* : Ø childhood

valeur spécifique

une façon très simple : a very easy way • *la lune :* the moon • *le soleil :* the sun

108 1. La parole est d'argent, mais le silence est d'or.
2. L'appétit vient en mangeant.
3. L'attaque est la meilleure forme de défense.
4. Les extrêmes se touchent (*ou* se rejoignent).

5. Tant qu'il y a de la vie, il y a de l'espoir.

109 Dans les proverbes, l'article Ø désigne une généralité ; il est accompagné de noms dénombrables pluriels ou indénombrables singuliers.

110 1. red and yellow 2. red and yellow and black 3. black and white 4. white and red 5. yellow and white

111 warm weather : généralité, nom indénombrable assimilé aux noms de saison

Lex : nom propre, autodéterminé

dogs : nom dénombrable pluriel associé de façon distributive à *people*

night : nom dénombrable employé au singulier

things : généralité, nom dénombrable au pluriel

people : collectif pluriel, généralité

strange people : collectif pluriel, l'adjectif crée une classe de *people*

parks : généralité, nom dénombrable au pluriel

dog : emploi qualitatif, c'est l'idée de chien qui est envisagée, déterminant Ø associé à un nom dénombrable au singulier.

> Dans la dernière phrase, la question posée est une généralité et toutes les formes nominales ont donc une détermination de type générique.

112 1. German 2. Irish English 3. Norwegian 4. Portuguese 5. Welsh

113 The Greeks come from **Greece** and speak **Greek.** The Dutch come from **the Netherlands** and speak **Dutch.** The Poles come from **Poland** and speak **Polish.** The Swedes come from **Sweden** and speak **Swedish.** Russians come from **Russia** and speak **Russian. Rumanians (Roumanians** *ou* **Romanians)** come from **Rumania (Romania** *ou* **Roumania)** and speak **Rumanian (Roumanian** *ou* **Romanian).** The French come from **France** and speak **French.** The Finns come from **Finland** and speak **Finnish.** The Japanese come from **Japan** and speak **Japanese.**

114 the Atlantic (nom d'océan) • the Congo (pays et fleuve ; on trouve aussi : Ø *Congo*) • the Maldives (îles) • the Mediterranean (nom de mer) • the United Kingdom (nom commun : *kingdom*) • the United Arab Emirates (nom commun : *emirates*)

115 The Rocky mountains are in the USA. • Lake Winnipeg is in Manitoba, Canada. • Belfast is in Northern Ireland. • Melbourne is in Australia. • Soweto is in South Africa. • The Kalahari desert is in the south of Africa. • Mount Etna is in Sicily. • The Isle of Wight is near the south coast of England, in the Channel.

116 1. an honest… 2. a one-way… 3. an honour 4. a *ou* an heroic… (h *peu prononcé car accent sur la deuxième syllabe*) 5. an hour 6. a university 7. an heir… 8. a *ou* an historical…(h *peu prononcé car accent sur la deuxième syllabe*) 9. a European 10. an honourable…

117 a loaf/a slice/a piece of bread • a slice/a slab *(une grosse tranche)*/a sliver *(une fine tranche)* of cake • a piece of chalk • a bar/a slab/a square/a piece of chocolate • a piece of evidence • a block of ice • a sheet/a piece/a scrap of paper • a grain of rice • a flake of snow • a cake/a bar of soap

118 a speck of dust • a clod of earth • a sliver/a pane of glass • a peal of laughter *(un éclat de rire)* • a drop of rain • a chunk of rock • a puff/a wisp of smoke • a means of transport

119 *A/an* est utilisé dans sa valeur générique. Il n'y a pas d'équivalent strict entre français et anglais dans la traduction des proverbes. Ils témoignent de deux cultures différentes et l'on peut noter ici que l'anglais utilise des données concrètes là où le français préfère l'abstraction.

120 1. My father's a joiner, my mother an accountant and I am a law student.
2. I go to the cinema (*ou* US: movies) with a friend twice a week.
3. Before being a gardener, he was a teacher for ten years.

4. That cake is as hard as a rock.

5. As a pilot, let me give you this piece of advice: make sure you haven't got a flat tyre.

6. She never swims without a buoy.

121 1. such a 2. such. 3. Such a 4. such an 5. such 6. such a 7. Such 8. such

122 1. You have **such a** beautiful <u>garden</u>! *[dénombrable singulier]*

2. **What a** <u>bunch</u> of <u>liars</u>! *[dénombrable singulier/dénombrable pluriel]*

3. You always have **such** heavy <u>luggage</u>! *[indénombrable]*

4. **What a** <u>bore</u>! *[dénombrable singulier]*

5. **What a** <u>pity</u> you couldn't come! *[indénombrable]*

> *Pity* et *shame* font partie des rares noms indénombrables précédés de *a* après *what* (§ 384).

6. That was **such** <u>fun</u>! *[indénombrable]*

123 1. It's too incredible a story. – I can't believe such an incredible story.

2. It's too abstract an explanation. – I can't understand such an abstract explanation.

3. It's too expensive a trip. – I can't afford such an expensive trip.

4. It's too hard a loaf of bread. – I can't cut such a hard loaf of bread.

5. It's too high a mountain. – I can't climb such a high mountain.

124 1. a) *few* : peu de gens, nombre insuffisant

b) *a few* : quelques personnes, vision positive, optimiste des choses

2. a) *few* : constat négatif du nombre peu élevé des personnes arrivées ; on en espérait plus

b) *a few* : les gens commencent à arriver, vision positive

3. a) *little* : mes connaissances sont rares, voire inexistantes

b) *a little* : vision positive de ce que je sais ; euphémisme utilisé par modestie peut-être, par quelqu'un qui sait beaucoup de choses.

4. a) *little* : il en reste peu et c'est dommage

b) *a little* : il en reste encore un peu et c'est bien.

125 1. I only know few things about his (*ou* her) life.

2. He is no doctor to me.

3. Could I have a little cold water in my coffee? It's too hot.

4. She isn't a very good cook.

5. I only have a few things to tell you.

6. She drove me back home in no time.

126 [ðə] 5. the university 6. the hospital 7. the horrible mistake 8. the historical landmark 11. the C.D. players 12. the hair 14. the ewe 15. the hotel

[ði] 1. the honest proposal 2. the honour 3. the expensive clothes 4. the hour 9. the umbrella 10. the I.C.B.M. 13. the M.P.

127 1. the floor (b) 2. The sky (b) 3. the airport (a) – the city (c) 4. The customer (e) 5. the door (b) 6. the piano (b) 7. the school (d) 8. The best of friends (e)

128 1. **The** President of France is meeting **the** English Prime Minister today. 2. **The** man who's playing **the** cello in **the** orchestra is my husband. 3. **The** World cup drew tourists from all over **the** world to **the** country. 4. All **the** people who were able to attend **the** matches were delighted. 5. Your visit has made **the** letter I had meant to write superfluous. 6. I like bathing in **the** Mediterranean and sleeping in **the** sun. 7. All **the** people on strike had gathered in **the** hall of **the** building in Regent Street and no one could get inside **the** office-block.

129 **The** sun rose up, at first like **a** yellow ball, then like **a** disk of polished brass. Trees, cornfields, farms, pastures, horses and workmen in **the** fields, all appeared instantly bathed in **a** soft light. Objects **a** great distance away, little towers, smoking chimneys. Slowly **the** dew became visible, hanging upon **the** trees like ladies' earrings. Soon everything was under **a** warm stillness.

130 1. He hoped that **his** fame and popularity would stop **his** creditors from asking for **their** money. 2. "Pleased to meet you! I read

your article in *Newsweek* on the plane," I said, and I went on telling him I was fascinated by **his** style. 3. She took a seat opposite **her** husband. 4. She was very proud of **her** house, **her** furniture, but not much of **her** husband. 5. I looked at the two women but decided not to make any comment about **their** make-up or **their** hair.

131 1. You're the sort of young man we want. 2. By the time she came round to the apartment the following afternoon, he had realized the truth.
3. He disappeared into the bathroom. There he cleaned his teeth, dropped the toothbrush into its mug and brushed his hair.
4. Then he returned to the bedroom and threw himself on the bed.
5. His final words as he closed the door behind him were lost in the noise of (the) traffic.

132 1. The car skidded across the gravel in front of the house, coming to a halt in the flowerbed just below the kitchen window.
2. A second later the van came crashing into the back of her car, slamming it against the wall of the house and shattering the glass in the kitchen window.
3. When she reached the far end of the gallery, she became aware of an office in which a short, balding man, wearing an old tweed jacket and corduroy trousers, was examining a picture.
4. His occupation, as described in his passport, was banker.
5. He was the branch manager of Barclays Bank in St Albans, Hertfordshire, which in banking circles is about the equivalent of being a captain in the Royal Air Force.

133 I knew Louise before she married. She was then a frail, delicate girl with large and melancholy eyes. Her father and mother loved her with an anxious adoration, because some illness, scarlet fever, I think, left her with a weak heart and she had to take the greatest care of herself. […] She'd been to all the best heart specialists in the world, and they all said that her life hung on a thread. But she had an unconquerable spirit.

16 Les démonstratifs

This/these : ce qui est proche, ce que l'on aime, le présent immédiat, ce qui va être expliqué par la suite.
That/those : ce qui est terminé, ce qui vient d'être dit, le passé, ce qui est éloigné dans le temps, ce que l'on n'aime pas du tout, ce qui est éloigné dans l'espace.

134 these men • those days • these mice • those geese • this news *ou* these pieces / items of news • those peoples (« *ces peuples* » ≠ those people : « *ces gens* ») • these leaves • those chiefs

135 1. This coming year will be fantastic. 2. This crossroads is dangerous. 3. This species is rare. 4. This analysis is wrong. 5. This phenomenon seldom happens.

136 1. That barracks has to disappear. 2. This aircraft is too old. 3. Check that data, please (data *s'emploie maintenant comme nom singulier ou pluriel* : that data is *ou* those data are). 4. This church is magnificent. 5. Where have you put that key?

137 (**d** : déterminant – **p** : pronom)
1. these days (**d**): unité de temps appartenant au présent du locuteur. 2. this climate (**d**) : élément de la situation dans laquelle se trouve le locuteur. 3. these mountains (**d**) : désigne un élément proche dans l'espace. 4. this (**p**) : présentation d'une personne. 5. this (**p**) : annonce un segment à droite.

138 (**d** : déterminant – **p** : pronom)
1. that (**p**) : renvoie à toute la proposition précédente. 2. that (**p**) : renvoie à tout ce qui a été dit avant – that plane (**d**) : distance affective, négative 3. that face (**d**) : distance affective, péjorative – that (**p**) : renvoie à la totalité de l'énoncé prononcé par l'interlocuteur précédent. 4. that (**p**) : renvoie à toute la proposition précédente. 5. that feeling (**d**) : renvoie à une sensation déjà ressentie avant, et avec une nuance péjorative.

139 1. These flowers are beautiful!
2. I can't carry all those books! Help me.

3. Can you really run that fast?

4. In those days there was no electricity.

5. This is Tim Parsons, my best friend.

6. I don't like this one.

7. You believe I am a traitor, is that it?

8. Those from London will arrive later.

9. Those we bought last month were perfect.

10. Those in the first row may stand up.

140 1. Avec ce clair de lune, je peux guider mon avion au travers des cols sans problème, ce qui a toujours été la partie la plus dangereuse de l'opération.

2. Personne n'oserait passer une nuit à la belle étoile dans cet endroit.

3. Il était difficile de ne pas aimer un tel homme.

4. C'est aussi simple que cela.

5. Les paysans le vénèrent, ce qui joue énormément en faveur de notre cause.

6. Cette petite aventure fera une lecture des plus intéressantes.

7. J'ai entendu parler de cette cérémonie. Peu de voyageurs ont la chance de la voir.

17 Les quantifieurs

141 1. Both my friends 2. Both of them 3. Both her sons 4. The two *[= ils se sont épousés]* – Both *[= ils se sont mariés chacun de leur côté]* 5. The two of them (*ou* both of them)

142 1. Both of these books 2. the two (*ou* both) 3. My two parents 4. Both his parents 5. both

143 1. I can't choose, I love both of them (*ou* I love them both).

2. Make up your mind! You can't marry the two, it's either one or the other.

3. But they are both so charming!

4. Either you get married or you remain single!

5. Either one would do in fact.

6. You can *not* get married. I am not married either.

7. But both my parents insist.

8. Both of them are wrong (*ou* They are both wrong).

9. Either I obey them or I leave home.

10. I'm sure you wouldn't like that either.

144 1. Vous pouvez prendre l'une ou l'autre rue pour aller à l'hôpital *(quantifieur)*.

2. Elle sait écrire des deux mains *(quantifieur)*.

3. C'est le genre d'homme qu'on aime ou qu'on déteste *(conjonction)*.

4. Elle ne l'aimait pas. Moi non plus *(adverbe)*.

5. J'ai vécu à Londres et à Detroit, mais je n'aime pas beaucoup ces deux villes (aucune de ces deux villes) *(quantifieur)*.

145 1. I feel both 2. They're either 3. Both these 4. Both solutions 5. either her 6. We both said 7. have either

146 1. both 2. both 3. Both 4. both 5. both 6. either 7. both 8. both

147 all these people • all my friends • all the papers • all those nice things • all three men • all these new methods • all your life • all her money

▎**All** *est toujours devant le groupe nominal.*

148 1. Tous les chiens sont des animaux, mais tous les animaux ne sont pas des chiens.

2. Toutes les personnes que vous avez rencontrées sont des amis à moi.

3. Les cinq enfants sont tous bons musiciens.

4. Toute laine tend à rétrécir.

5. Vous avez eu tout le plaisir et eux tout le travail difficile.

6. Toutes ces lettres doivent être postées avant cinq heures ce soir.

7. Ils ont travaillé dur tout l'été.

8. Nous avons attendu tout ce temps.

9. Ils étaient absents toute la semaine dernière.

10. Ils sont arrivés en toute hâte.

149 1. Elle ne cuisine pas si bien que cela. 2. Je n'aurais jamais pensé que vous, et surtout vous, l'apprécieriez. 3. Tous les spectateurs ont applaudi le spectacle. 4. Tout ceci t'appartient désormais. 5. Elle était tout de blanc vêtue. 6. Elle était toute bouleversée par ces mauvaises nouvelles. 7. Le score était de deux partout. 8. Il va vous falloir travailler d'autant plus dur après deux semaines d'absence (Vous allez devoir mettre les bouchées doubles…).

150 1. All things come to those who wait. 2. All's for the best in the best of all possible worlds. 3. All that glitters is not gold. 4. All's well that ends well. 5. It's all or nothing.

151 1. all day 2. The whole school 3. On the whole 4. all smiles 5. All I'm asking for 6. as a whole 7. All I could do 8. the whole world

152 1. has 2. costs 3. is 4. brings 5. is

153 (**d** : déterminant – **p** : pronom) each coming day **(d)** • thirty pound each **(p)** • each one **(d)** • each of you **(p)** • each of the dogs **(p)**

154 1. They **each** had a suitcase to carry. 2. **Every** one (*ou* each one) did as they wanted. 3. I saw these two films last week. **Each** of them has a definite appeal. 4. Take one **each**. 5. I met her twice. It was **each** time a pleasure.

155 1. all day • every day • each day 2. all 3. each • every 4. the whole 5. all

156 1. *Remplacement impossible.* 2. He has read every novel I have given him. 3. The policemen wanted to know every detail of her timetable. 4. *Remplacement impossible.* 5. Every fellow-student of hers was present at the meeting.

> *On ne peut remplacer* all *par* every *que quand* all *est suivi d'un nom au pluriel.*

157 1. C'est l'exception qui confirme la règle. 2. On ne peut pas plaire à tout le monde. 3. Toute chose a une fin. 4. Il y a un temps et un lieu pour chaque chose. 5. À chacun ses défauts.

158 1. much time 2. many people 3. much courage 4. much work 5. enough is enough 6. much courage 7. many opportunities 8. much worth 9. had enough 10. many children

159 1. a lot to do 2. Many people 3. enough problems 4. cost a lot 5. A good many people 6. A good deal of their work 7. There's plenty more gravy 8. enough water 9. so much salt 10. There isn't much

160 1. déterminant 2. adverbe 3. déterminant 4. déterminant 5. pronom 6. déterminant 7. déterminant – pronom 8. adverbe 9. pronom 10. pronom

161 1. some tea 2. Ø vegetables 3. some Mr Smith 4. Some people 5. some meal!

162 1. [səm] 2. [sʌm] 3. [səm] 4. [sʌm] 5. [sʌm] 6. [sʌm] 7. [sʌm] 8. [sʌm] 9. [sʌm] 10. [sʌm]

> *Some* se prononce [səm] en 1 et 3 car il est suivi d'un nom et il signifie « du », « de la », « des » ou « quelques ».

163 1. If you need some [sʌm], there's some [səm] ice left in the fridge. 2. Do you know you have left some [səm] money on the living-room table? 3. Some [sʌm] children were playing tennis while others were having a swim in the river. 4. She was reading some [sʌm] sort of newspaper. 5. He is *some* [sʌm] chess player!

164 1. déterminant 2. adverbe 3. pronom 4. déterminant 5. pronom 6. déterminant 7. adverbe 8. déterminant 9. déterminant 10. adverbe

165 1. any 2. any 3. some 4. any 5. any 6. some. 7. some – some

166 1. some 2. some 3. any 4. Some 5. Any 6. any 7. some – any 8. some

167 1. any – *Tu veux des abricots, mais je ne pense pas qu'il en reste.* 2. any – *Dis-moi combien tu en as, si tu en as.* 3. some – *J'ai fait une tarte aux pommes. Tu en veux ?* 4. any – *Je suis désolé(e) mais je ne peux pas marcher plus vite.* 5. Some – *Certaines des maisons ont été détruites par l'inondation.*

168 1. some – *Elle a gagné dans les deux mille livres en pariant sur les (des) chevaux*

2. any – *Je pense qu'elle n'ira jamais mieux.*
3. some – *Encore un peu de gâteau ?*
4. Some – *Certains de ses amis sont de vrais marginaux.*
5. any – *Je ne ferai pas un pas de plus.*

169 a few people • a little water • a few houses • a little wine • a few sheep • a little time • a few times • a little fish *(un peu de poisson* – a few fish : *quelques poissons)* • a little faster • a few criteria • a little chicken • a few series • a few mice • a little love • a little help

| *Attention, ne pas confondre* a little *quantifieur (un peu de) et* little *adjectif (= small, petit).*

170 1. I have few reliable friends.
2. I'm a little afraid of him.
3. I have a few good reasons not to like him.
4. Couldn't you drive a little faster?
5. You will need a little patience.

171 1. There are a few problems left to solve.
2. Give me a few explanations.
3. I'm seeing too few people these days.
4. I have too little time off to spend a few days with you.
5. I know little about her.

172 1. no fool 2. no sleep 3. is none 4. no ordinary 5. for nothing

173 1. none of 2. nothing to do 3. for no 4. no woman 5. than nothing.

174 1. no questions – no lies. 2. Believe nothing 3. than none. 4. none so deaf 5. nothing new

175 **137,000 people:** one hundred and thirty-seven thousand people • **0.9143:** nought point nine one four three • **40,000,000 inhabitants:** forty million inhabitants • **3.7853:** three point seven eight five three • **0.394:** nought point three nine four • **2.205:** two point two nought five • **378:** three hundred and seventy-eight • **499:** four hundred and ninety-nine • **219.98:** two hundred and nineteen point nine eight. **29,028:** twenty-nine thousand and twenty-eight

| *On peut utiliser* zero *à la place de* nought, *notamment en anglais américain.*

176 **an inch:** 2,54 cm • **a foot:** 30,48 cm • **a yard:** 0,914 m • **a mile:** 1,609 km • **an acre:** 40,47 a • **a pint:** 0,57 l • **an ounce:** 28,35 g • **a pound:** 453,59 g • **a stone:** 6,35 kg • **a gallon:** 3,785 l

177 **1 cm :** 0.394 inch • **1 m :** 3.280 ft • **1 km :** 0.621 mile • **1 l :** 1.1760 pint • **1 kg :** 2.205 lb • **1cm^2:** 0.155 sq. inch • **1 ha :** 2.471 acres • **1km^2:** 0.386 sq. mile • **1 cm^3:** 0.061 cubic inch • **1m^3:** 219.98 gallons

178 **00 44 18187498523:** 0 0 (*ou* double O) four four (*ou* double four) one eight one eight seven four nine eight five two three

00 44 01634556588: 0 0 (*ou* double O) four four (*ou* double four) 0 one six three four five five (*ou* double five) six five eight eight (*ou* double eight)

00 33 10356065079: 0 0 (*ou* double O) three three (*ou* double three) one 0 three five six 0 six five 0 seven nine

00 33 02326007057: 0 0 (*ou* double O) three three (*ou* double three) 0 two three two six 0 0 (*ou* double O) seven 0 five seven

| *Sous l'influence américaine, on dit de plus en plus* zero *à la place de* 0 *(zéro prononcé comme la lettre O).*

179 November the third, nineteen fifty-three

October the seventeenth, nineteen eighty-five

May the twenty-first, nineteen seventy-nine

March the twenty-seventh, nineteen eighty-eight

January the eleventh, two thousand and eight

September the second, two thousand and eighteen.

18 Relier deux noms

180 1. to my 2. cheque for 3. article from 4. on a quest for 5. to (*ou* in) the garage. 6. in African art 7. on strike – in wages 8. to every 9. from the other 10. to (*ou* for) 11. on a tour – by night 12. to the manager

181 France's foreign policy • the children's toys • my parents' friends • the President's men • Jenny and Peter's wedding party • Dickens's novels *ou* Dickens' novels • Ulysses' travels • today's weather report • anyone's guess

182 1. possession • 2. possession • 3. catégorie • 4. durée • 5. possession ou catégorie • 6. unité de temps • 7. possession • 8. possession • 9. possession • 10. possession

183 1. my brother's yellow eyes 2. today's newspaper 3. Saint Peter's cathedral 4. Merlin's magic 5. Dublin's fair city center

184 1. my father's eyes 2. Mary's book 3. Spielberg's films 4. ten years' imprisonment 5. a butcher's knife

185 jewels at the jeweller's (*ou* US : jeweler's) • flowers at the florist's • chicken at the poulterer's • tomatoes at the greengrocer's • shoes at the shoemaker's • material at the draper's • cigarettes at the tobacconist's • meat at the butcher's • hats at the hatter's • medicine at the chemist's • thread and needles at the haberdasher's • pans at the ironmonger's • tins at the grocer's

186 1. my sister's (*sous entendu* : my sister's **in-laws** 2. the dentist's (*sous-entendu* : the dentist's **surgery**) 3. St John's (*sous-entendu* : St John's **hospital**) – *connaissance culturelle* 4. the jeweller's (*sous-entendu* : the jeweller's **shop**) 5. Ulysses's (*sous-entendu* : Ulysses's (*ou* Ulysses') **adventures** were incredible adventures) – *emploi littéraire, la répétition est évitée par avance.* 6. the lady's (*sous-entendu* : the lady's **bike** *déjà mentionné*)

187 1. Il est maintenant hors de danger. 2. Les deux jeunes enfants de la pauvre femme ont été légèrement blessés dans l'accident.
3. Ce monstre avait des pattes de chèvre et des ailes de corbeau.
4. Cela nous a pris une journée entière de travail.
5. L'activité favorite de ma grand-mère paternelle était de se rendre chez le libraire.
6. Cet ami de Jenny a des yeux de démon et un visage d'ange.
7. Pour l'amour du ciel, tiens-toi bien !
8. Es-tu déjà allé(e) chez Sotheby's ?

188 1. Let me introduce **the chieftain's two young children**.
2. I'd been hoping that **that contractor's workers** could help me build my house.
3. The nurse had finished bandaging **the wounded man's head**.
4. pas de génitif : qualifie *joy*
5. pas de génitif : expression proverbiale
6. pas de génitif : *smell* et *disinfectant* désignent la même chose ; relation partie/tout.
7. pas de génitif : *article* et *clothing* désignent la même chose ; relation partie/tout
8. pas de génitif : *knowledge* est déjà précédé d'un déterminant possessif (*her* = the woman's)
9. pas de génitif : adjectif substantivé
10. pas de génitif : *end* et *corridor* désignent la même chose ; relation partie/tout

189 1. this boy's problem
2. the end of the century
3. last year's wine
4. the leg of the table
5. a mother's duty

190 milk chocolate: chocolate made with milk • chocolate milk: milk flavoured with chocolate

malt whisky: whisky made with malt
whisky malt: malt used to make whisky

a race horse: a horse that runs in races
a horse race: a race for horses

a vegetable garden: a garden where you grow vegetables
garden vegetables: vegetables that grow in a garden

bag leather: leather used to make bags
a leather bag: a bag mad of leather

191 **address-book:** a book in which you write addresses • **bank account:** an account in a bank • **daydream** *(rêverie)*: a dream during the day • **fingertip:** the tip of the finger • **handshake:** when you shake hands with someone • **money box** *(tirelire)*: a box in which you put money • **leather coat:** a coat made of leather

192 mouse-traps • on-lookers • corkscrews • grown-ups • race-horses

193 **a blood transfusion :** une transfusion sanguine
an oak forest : une forêt de chênes
a story-teller : un conteur, une conteuse
a dining-room : une salle à manger
an all-day session : une séance d'une journée entière

19 Les adjectifs

194 1. her crazy ideas 2. considerable interest in various circles 3. no conceivable practical application 4. his greatest love 5. a pleasant, white-painted house 6. the great white peaks 7. A strange, fatalistic calm 8. Her long woollen dress 9. the high grassy bank

195 1. The handsome tall seventeen-year-old French boy 2. A rather common tiny wooden cane chair 3. that old-fashioned grey flannel shirt 4. a flashy brand-new black sports car 5. a very expensive rather large black leather bag

196 1. All this is but <u>mere</u> coincidence *(épithète)*. 2. Could you say something <u>nice</u>, for a change *(épithète = a nice thing)*? 3. This <u>first</u> edition of the novel is quite <u>unique</u> (first *épithète* – unique *attribut*). 4. It's totally <u>impossible</u>, I'm <u>sorry</u> *(attribut – attribut)*. 5. His *(ou* Her) face was a little too <u>white</u> *(attribut)*. 6. The plan was far too <u>ambitious</u>. *(attribut)* *(ou* It was far too ambitious a plan). 7. Mind you, my memory is as <u>good</u> as yours *(attribut)*.

8. These apricots are not <u>ripe</u> enough to be eaten now *(attribut)*. 9. Don't worry, it happened by <u>sheer</u> accident *(épithète)*. 10. This question is too <u>difficult</u> for me *(attribut)* *(ou* It's too difficult a question for me).

197 1. **essential :** peut être épithète ou attribut 2. **sheer :** ne peut être qu'épithète 3. **content :** ne peut être qu'attribut 4. **much :** n'est pas un adjectif mais un quantifieur

198 1. un verre à vin plein – un verre rempli de vin 2. la seule pièce disponible (pas de différence entre les deux structures) 3. les gens en question – les gens soucieux 4. l'explication compliquée – l'explication en cause 5. Vous avez rencontré la bonne personne. – Vous avez rencontré la personne proprement dite.

199 1. angry with – for 2. afraid of 3. anxious about 4. cross with 5. cross about 6. dear to 7. desperate for 8. even with 9. grateful to – for helping 10. heavy with

200 1. nasty 2. new 3. oblivious 4. open 5. petrified 6. pressed 7. proud 8. quick 9. sure 10. scared

201 1. all the people present were amused 2. even someone as blasé as my brother looked astonished 3. the most optimistic of the viewers can't help feeling depressed. 4. I still couldn't sleep, I was so frightened! 5. I went to see him at the end and told him how interested I was. 6. I saw on the doctor's face that he too felt worried. 7. anybody listening to him grows fascinated. 8. even the most attentive pupils got bored.

202 1. well-fed 2. home-made 3. long-legged 4. well-mannered 5. heart-broken – heart-breaking 6. a corn-producing country 7. an expensive-looking car 8. a never-ending story 9. left-handed

203 1. a ten-minute rest 2. a two-month holiday 3. a fifty-year-old man 4. a forty-page magazine 5. a sixty-litre tank 6. a two-thousand dollar answer 7. a ten-mile walk

204 1. The blind, the deaf, the dumb 2. the Blacks – the Whites 3. the young and the old 4. the under-fourteens 5. The Welsh – the English

205 1. Some parking spaces are reserved for the use of the disabled. 2. The homeless are more and more numerous nowadays. 3. Three young people out of four like going to the movies. 4. The difficult is done at once, the impossible takes a little longer. 5. The dumb can't communicate with the blind through sign language. 6. Darwin expounded his theory of "the survival of the fittest" in a book called *The Origin of Species*.

20 Les comparatifs et les superlatifs

206 1. His hair was not as (*ou* so) black as a raven's wing. 2. My sister works in the same hospital as my father. 3. Her necklace is twice as long as mine. 4. I make as many mistakes as my neighbour. 5. I've had a quarter as many sweets as my little sister. 6. She likes going to the theatre as much as he does (*ou* as him).

207 1. Don't buy this book! It is four times as expensive here as in the other bookshop (*ou* four times more expensive than). 2. I have got as many friends as you (have). 3. Unfortunately she is not as clever as she looks. 4. She speaks as good English as a BBC announcer. 5. Could you speak half as fast so that I could understand twice as quickly? 6. In this weather we are as well here as outside. 7. I don't think she is that cross (*ou* as cross as that). 8. Stop doing the same as me over and over again.

208 1. happier 2. spicier and tastier (*ou* more spicy and more tasty) 3. more intelligent 4. nearer – heavier 5. elder 6. more angry 7. more smashing 8. narrower (*ou* more narrow)

209 bigger • fatter • wider • deeper • higher • narrower (*ou* more narrow) • feebler (*ou* more feeble) • heavier • more handsome • more right • truer • better • more wrong • worse • more real • thinner • more meager • more acid • fairer • older *ou* elder

210 1. If you're not more careful in the future, I won't buy you anything any more. 2. It's far easier than you think. 3. If you ask me, she's more stupid than nasty. 4. I've never known anyone richer than him. 5. All this seems more real to me now, I found it difficult to believe. 6. Your insight is more right than you think. 7. I won't go any farther; my legs are more tired than the rest of me. 8. He wouldn't let me read any further. 9. They arrived later than the others but not last. 10. I saw Tim and Tom last week: the former has grown bigger and the latter thinner.

211 1. It's getting harder and harder to find someone you can really trust. 2. His speech was so long that the audience felt less and less interested. 3. Means of communication are becoming quicker and quicker. 4. It was pouring outside and I was less and less in a hurry to leave. 5. Going on holiday costs more and more money. 6. Village schools have fewer and fewer pupils. 7. She was more and more pleased as she heard the nice speech of the manager. 8. More and more people use the Internet. 9. The imaginary world was getting more and more (*ou* less and less) real. 10. There are fewer and fewer hitchhikers on the roads these days.

212 1. The more I know you, the less I appreciate your company. 2. The more he earns, the more he spends. 3. The older she gets, the more beautiful she is. 4. The dearer her clothes, the less they suit her. 5. The harder you try, the better it is. 6. The more friends he has, the happier he feels. 7. The earlier you come, the sooner we leave. 8. The more he loves her, the more she loathes him. 9. The more drinks you have, the more dangerous you become. 10. The farther he goes, the fewer chances he has of coming back.

213 1. Mieux vaut faire envie que pitié. 2. Mieux vaut tard que jamais. 3. L'herbe est toujours plus verte de l'autre côté. 4. Plus on est de fous, plus on rit. 5. Mieux vaut prévenir que guérir. 6. Plus vite ce sera commencé, plus vite ce sera fini.

214 1. This is the nicest piece of news of the day. 2. He is the most famous senator in Congress. 3. That's the worst place Ø I know. 4. China is the most populated area in the world. 5. It's the strangest remark Ø I have ever heard. 6. This is the best ever book in the history of literature.

21 Les pronoms personnels et possessifs

215 1. He used to bring her flowers every other day. 2. The milkman brought them milk every morning. 3. Could you give them my share? 4. All her friends gave her presents for her child's birth. 5. She had promised him a few things so that he would not go. 6. I send them my best regards. 7. They never showed him their holiday photographs. 8. I had to teach them linguistics. 9. He was supposed to tell them the truth. 10. She gave it to him (*ou* her).

216 1. She wondered whether she should go or stay with him (*ou* her *ou* them). 2. She asked the two of them if they could give her a hand. 3. They said to me that I should be more careful because I had hurt my leg again. 4. He said to them to mind their own business from then on. 5. She started by saying that in that novel, she had tried to show what her life was (*ou* had been) in those days. 6. She shouted to him that he'd better hurry or they'd be late!

217 1. Nobody except you knows where she is. So *you* are going to go and fetch her. 2. "Who bought all this?" "I did." "You did!" "Yes, it is I (*ou* me) who went shopping (ou *I* went shopping)." 3. "I haven't met them yet. Have you?" "I saw them yesterday." 4. I'm fed up with him. He's getting on my nerves. 5. He is three times as big as she is (*ou* as her) and yet she eats twice as much as he does (*ou* as him). 6. The doorbell's ringing. It must be her. She's always late when she visits us. 7. "What's your cat's name?" "Kitty. She is really independent." 8. It's her father who wants to speak to her on the phone, but she isn't here and he won't believe me when I tell him. 9. "Who said, 'You never know.' (*ou* 'One never knows.')?" "What I know is (that) it isn't me!" 10. "We are arriving from New York." "Pleased to meet you. *We* are arriving from Cuba."

218 1. Il est important que tu le saches. (annonce)
2. Je ne pourrai pas venir à ton mariage et je te prie de m'en excuser. (reprise)
3. Il m'a été très difficile de croire que tu ne le savais pas non plus. (annonce – reprise)
4. C'est gentil à toi de le faire à ma place. (annonce – reprise)
5. J'ai pensé qu'il valait mieux t'en parler en premier. (verbe d'appréciation – reprise)
6. Cela ne fait rien, d'ailleurs, je m'en fiche. (impersonnel – reprise)
7. Il était évident que personne ne trouvait essentiel de le vendre. (annonce – verbe d'appréciation – reprise)
8. Si c'est si facile à faire, pourquoi ne le fais-tu pas toi-même ? (reprise – reprise)
9. C'est toujours celui qui parle en dernier qui a raison. (impersonnel)

219 1. mine – mine 2. yours – mine 3. theirs – hers 4. ours 5. yours – theirs – his

220 1. Ton soi-disant médecin, tu ne penses pas qu'il ressemble étrangement au nôtre ?
2. Elle me regardait avec ce sourire dans les yeux qui n'appartient qu'à elle.
3. Prends le leur si tu n'as pas le tien, mais en aucun cas je ne te prêterai le mien *[le pluriel et le féminin sont également possibles]*.
4. Amène tes enfants, les miens seront ravis de jouer avec les tiens.
5. Leur maison est une très belle maison, rien à voir avec la sienne à lui.

221 1. Rien de sérieux ! C'est juste un ami à moi… 2. As-tu dit à ton espèce de mari de se dépêcher ? À cause de sa mollesse habituelle, nous allons être en retard ! 3. Mon diamant à moi, comme lui dit-on, est bien plus authentique que le sien à elle. 4. Ses cheveux à lui sont bouclés naturellement, pas les miens. 5. Entre les tiens, les leurs et les miens, je choisirai toujours mes propres enfants !

222 1. Un jour, tu comprendras qu'il vaut mieux avoir un ami sûr que dix bons copains. 2. Je voudrais une très belle rose rouge, s'il vous plaît. C'est pour la femme de ma vie. 3. Tu as dit un million, pas un million deux cents ? Comment as-tu pu faire une telle erreur ? 4. Mon seul et unique loisir, c'est de faire une partie de squash de temps en temps. 5. Elle a eu des jumeaux. L'un est un garçon, l'autre une fille et ils ont tous les deux un grain de beauté sur la joue droite. 6. Quelles pêches voulez-vous ? Des vertes et des pas mûres, comme d'habitude ? 7. Ma voiture est trop petite, il va me falloir en acheter une plus grande. 8. Un plus un plus un égalent trois.

223 1. these (ones) 2. these blue ones – those green ones 3. the ones that **are** 4. these (ones) **look** – the ones 5. the ones … **have** – those ugly ones.

■ *These ones* est familier (§ 199).

224 1. You should have been told I would be late! 2. Shall we go? Are you ready? Hurry up or we'll miss the beginning of the film! 3. So you're happy with your trip, my boy? 4. What horrible weather we had in July! 5. Someone called you this morning. 6. The management say they are going to fire the two secretaries. 7. I was (*ou* have been) asked to write this report for tomorrow. 8. We really had fun yesterday. And you, what did *you* do? 9. Three people are reported to have been seriously wounded.

225 1. On ne dirait jamais qu'il a plu autant l'été dernier. 2. On dit qu'on lui a fait avouer des crimes dont on n'avait jamais trouvé les auteurs. 3. On (te) l'a volé pendant que tu dormais ! On ne t'a jamais dit de fermer ta porte à clé ? 4. Tu sais, on ne sait jamais ce que le futur nous réserve. 5. On m'avait dit qu'on me couperait les cheveux en brosse mais on me les a laissés tels qu'ils étaient.

226 1. On essaiera de démontrer que deux et deux ne font pas toujours quatre. 2. On ne devrait jamais dire ces choses-là à quelqu'un de déprimé ! 3. On t'attend à huit heures pile devant la gare. 4. Alors on a des choses à me dire ? Par quoi commence-t-on ? 5. On dit toujours que c'est dans le besoin que l'on reconnaît ses amis et c'est bien vrai.

22 Les pronoms réfléchis et réciproques

227 1. yourself (*ou* you) 2. herself 3. themselves 4. yourself 5. you 6. yourselves

228 1. him 2. them 3. herself 4. yourself (*ou* yourselves*) 5. him – himself 6. yourself

229 1. John and Mary kept looking at each other. 2. Brothers and sisters love one another. 3. They congratulated each other on their degrees. 4. We have never met. [*Attention, le verbe* meet *s'emploie sans pronom réciproque.*] 5. We send each other letters.

■ On peut utiliser *one another* à la place de *each other* et inversement.

230 1. The more I think of us, the more I think we should see each other less often. (*réciproque*)
2. They have lost the last match and they are really annoyed with themselves for it. (*réfléchi*)
3. She is ashamed of herself. (*réfléchi*)
4. There's nothing like trying to help one another. (*réciproque*)
5. People were talking to one another and I couldn't make myself heard. (*réciproque – réfléchi*)
6. Your book sells well, you can be proud of yourselves. (*réfléchi – le verbe* sell *[= se vendre] s'emploie sans pronom réciproque.*)
7. Relax, have a ten minute nap and when you wake up, you will feel very well. (*Ces verbes anglais ne nécessitent pas la présence du pronom réfléchi.*)
8. I'm going to congratulate myself if no one else does. (*réfléchi*)
9. I met the president himself and he showed an interest in what I did. (*réfléchi*)
10. She taught herself the piano./She learnt to play the piano all by herself. (*réfléchi*)

La phrase

23 L'ordre des mots dans la phrase simple

231 1. Hardly had it been raining when the hurricane hit the house. 2. Only then did I understand what he was saying. 3. Never shall we forgive them for what they did. 4. Often have I complained about it, but to no use. 5. Seldom have I seen so much happiness.

232 1. *No sooner* had she left her home than the sun started shining. 2. *Never before* has there been such a disaster. 3. *So angry* was I that I decided to write a letter to the director. 4. *Such* was my anger that I became speechless. 5. *Nowhere* was the boss to be seen. 6. *Not only* did he arrive late *but* he didn't even apologize. 7. *So* absurd was his conduct that they all laughed. 8. *Never before in my life* have I had such an idea. 9. *Well* do I remember your grandmother. 10. *On no account* are you to talk about it.

233 1. So have I. 2. So have you. 3. Nor (*ou* neither) can they. 4. So have you. 5. So did his girlfriend. 6. So shall (*ou* will) we. 7. So does her mother. 8. Nor (*ou* neither) can Pierre. 9. So did the others. 10. Nor (*ou* neither) had we.

234 1. Had he arrived earlier… 2. Should she arrive now… 3. Had he had a better idea… 4. Should you change your plan… 5. Should it start raining now… 6. Had they passed their exams…

235 "Perhaps it is too late to start our meeting."
"So it is indeed. So, we can decide to leave."
"But here comes our boss!"
"I'm sorry. There were so many trucks on the road! Among them was even a tractor! Never shall I forget that nightmare. No sooner had I left home than problems started. Had I known, I wouldn't have left home."
"Nor would we."

236 1. It was Annabel who wrote a love story when she was ten. 2. It was a love story that Annabel wrote when she was ten. 3. It was when she was ten that Annabel wrote a love story. 4. It's you, Mr President, who are telling us a lie. 5. It's to us that you're telling a lie, Mr President. 6. It's a lie that you're telling us, Mr President. 7. It was us (*très soutenu* : we) who understood what he did at that moment. 8. It was what he did that we understood at that moment. 9. It was at that moment that we understood what he did.

237 1. What Sophie's looking for is a new apartment. 2. What Steve wanted was a cheeseburger. 3. What she broke was a vase. 4. What they will like is Brooklyn Bridge. 5. What she has visited is New York. 6. What I might see is the parade in London. 7. What they want to buy is three copies of that book (*ou* What they want is to buy …). 8. What he says is that he's never felt that way before. 9. What Errol is sticking to is the idea that life is for living. 10. What I've never understood is what they liked about him.

238 1. Can she speak German? 2. Will he go to New Zealand next year? 3. Are you going out tonight? 4. Has the unemployment rate come down in Britain? 5. Do they prefer tea to coffee? 6. Do your parents never (*ou* ever) leave their country? 7. Do they have a nice house? 8. Would they rather stay inside? 9. Does Steve have many brothers and sisters? 10. Did Brenda say she'd be late?

239 1. Yes, she can. No, she can't. 2. Yes, he will. No, he won't. 3. Yes, I am. No, I am not. 4. Yes, it has. No, it hasn't. 5. Yes, they do. No, they don't. 6. Yes, they do (leave their country). No they don't (ever leave their country). 7. Yes, they do. No, they don't. 8. Yes, they would. No, they wouldn't. 9. Yes, he does. No, he doesn't. 10. Yes, she did. No, she didn't.

240 1. *What* happened? 2. *What* were you doing last night? 3. *Who* rang? 4. *Who* wants some more tea? 5. *Where* did she go? 6. *What* did they look at? 7. *How* did you do it? 8. *When* did they arrive? 9. *Who* left a note on my desk? 10. *When* did Omar live in California?

241 1. Who did you send the flowers to? (*très soutenu :* Whom) 2. Who did he rely on? (*très soutenu :* Whom) 3. Who did they care for? (*très soutenu :* Whom) 4. What was Carey listening to? 5. What was she thinking about? 6. Who did he think of? (*très soutenu :* Whom) 7. What did we both laugh at? 8. Whose doctor did you send for? 9. Whose house did the hooligans break into? 10. When did you say he would be back?

242 1. Their friends wonder where they are going.
2. Laurie wants to know who called.
3. I'd like to know when you will see her again.
4. Let's ask them who was on the phone.
5. Peter wants to know how old her grandparents are.
6. I'd be pleased to know what they bought.
7. I'm asking you why you are crying.
8. I'd be interested to know what you were listening to.
9. I'm just asking how you managed it.
10. Could you tell me why she ran away?

243 1. The policeman asked what they had been doing at that time the day before.
2. The librarian wanted to know which of these books she had liked best. 3. She enquired why Louise had lied to him. 4. She forced him to tell her where he would spend his holiday. 5. He was furious and asked her who (*très soutenu :* whom) she had been seeing.

244 1. How deep 2. How old 3. How high 4. How often 5. How many 6. How much 7. How long 8. How far 9. How long 10. How wide

245 1. espace 2. temps 3. temps 4. espace 5. temps 6. temps 7. temps 8. temps 9. temps 10. temps

Phrase 5 : Since when have you been learning Spanish? *Phrase 8* : Since when have they been married?

246 1. Quelle est la longueur du lac ?
2. Combien de temps comptez-vous rester ici ?

3. Pendant combien de temps as-tu vécu avec elle ?
4. Quelle est la longueur de la nouvelle voiture qu'il vient d'acheter ?
5. Depuis combien de temps apprends-tu l'espagnol ? *ou* Ça fait combien de temps que tu apprends l'espagnol ?
6. Est-ce qu'ils t'ont dit combien de temps ils ont passé en Afrique du Sud ?
7. Il y a combien de temps que leur famille est arrivée en Grande-Bretagne ?
8. Ils sont mariés depuis combien de temps ? *ou* Ça fait combien de temps qu'ils sont mariés ?
9. Je me demande combien de temps il va parler
10. Il vous a fallu combien de temps pour aller à Manchester en voiture ?

247 1. So, how are you today? 2. Do you know what his (*ou* her) mother is like? 3. How do you know he won't come? 4. How come he didn't tell you anything? 5. How did you learn about it? 6. How could I get him (*ou* her) to understand? 7. How do you want me to know it? 8. How did she do it? 9. Can you tell me what that guy is like? 10. How shall we do it?

248 1. What did 2. What would 3. What do you 4. What time 5. Which of 6. What is 7. What will 8. Which sentence 9. Which one 10. What will

249 "**Who's** that?" [...] "Oh, **what** do you want?" [...] "**What** do you mean, 'Hi'! Do you know **what** time it is?" "**What** does it matter? [...] "**Which** one?" "I don't care **which** one. Just call **who** you want." "OK, of John, Peter and Steve, **which** (*lequel*)/**who** (*qui*) should I call?" "[...] Talking of **which** (*à ce propos*), could you lend me your car?" "**Which** one? [...] But **what** happened to your own car?"

250 1. What's the weather like?
2. What are his (*ou* her) parents like?
3. How are your parents?
4. How long have they been in Germany?
5. Whose book is this? (*ou* Whose is this book?/Who does this book belong to?)

6. How long will they be in Scotland for? (*ou* How long will they stay in Scotland?)
7. When did it last rain? (*moins fréquent* : How long is it since it last rained?)
8. But, didn't you see that car?
9. I wonder how far (*ou* to what extent) he is really determined to succeed.
10. How likely is she to get her driving licence?

251 1. How nice it was to see you! 2. How she has changed over the years! 3. What a sweetheart you are! 4. How nice your cousin is! 5. What a fool he was not to listen to her advice! 6. How hot this tea is! 7. What a relief it was to see them! 8. How stupid this programme is! 9. How strange it feels not to be with my daughter! 10. What a fuss he made about nothing!

252 1. It was so great to see you! 2. I behaved in such a stupid way. 3. I have so much to study (*ou* I have to study so much). 4. It hurts so much to listen to you! 5. She was so mad at him! 6. I was such a fool to believe you! 7. He really cares so much for you (*ou* cares for you so much). 8. I'm sorry but I am in such a hurry!

253 1. There were so many mistakes that I couldn't read his paper. 2. We had such terrible weather that we decided to leave after an hour. 3. I was in such a hurry that I didn't notice the accident. 4. The book was so funny that I couldn't stop reading. 5. I was so late that it was useless to try to make it. 6. They were given so much wine to drink that they got drunk in less than an hour. 7. It rained so much that we decided to cut short our holiday. 8. It was such a lousy film that we didn't watch it to the end.

> *Il est possible à l'oral de ne pas utiliser la conjonction* **that** *dans ces phrases.*

254 1. What a fool 2. How (*ou* So) nice 3. such a hurry 4. so hard 5. How lovely 6. so many people 7. so much hair 8. so great 9. so much to offer 10. such bad manners

255 1. Don't they speak well! *Ce qu'ils parlent bien !*
2. Didn't they behave badly! *Comme ils se sont mal comportés !*
3. Aren't I smart! *Hein que je suis malin !*
4. Don't I know! *À qui le dites-vous !*
5. Isn't it clever! *Comme c'est intelligent !*
6. Isn't he old now! *Ce qu'il est vieux maintenant !*
7. Doesn't she look sweet! *Comme elle est mignonne !*
8. Doesn't time fly! *Comme le temps passe (vite) !*

24 Les constructions verbe + verbe

256 1. to leave 2. to tell 3. travelling 4. not to talk 5. driving 6. waiting 7. to listen 8. not having (*ou* not to have) 9. to give up 10. not to worry

257 When it was too late he decided **to tell** his Mum about his secret love affair. He knew how **not to shock** her and wanted **to be cautious** with her so as **not to cause** any problem. He is very sweet and hates **hurting** (*ou* to hurt) people's feelings but at the same time he couldn't bear **not to let her** (*ou* **not letting her**) **know**. So he asked her **to promise not to talk** while he was speaking. He had to wait **for her to sit up** in her bed and then started **to explain** (*ou* **explaining**) that he disliked **her prying** into his affairs and that he enjoyed **leading** his own life. He kept **talking** never daring **to look** at her. When he stopped **speaking** he realized that she was sound asleep.

258 1. I advise you not to write that letter. 2. They swear never to have stolen that bike. 3. They swear never to steal again. 4. My parents have always let me do anything I want. 5. I was listening very carefully. I heard her whisper (*ou* whispering) to her husband. 6. I distinctly remember him (*ou* his) taking your keys. 7. I would prefer not to see her right now. 8. I like listening (*ou* to listen) to opera. 9. I would like to listen to an opera. 10. I promise not to do it again.

259 1. Can you help me (to) fill in this form?
2. If you choose to stay, you will have to cooperate.
3. I like being admired. I would so much like to be admired.
4. I want you to tell me the truth.
5. You refuse to tell me where he is? (*ou* Won't you tell me where he is?).
6. You all agreed to see that film, didn't you?
7. In the end, we convinced (*ou* persuaded) her to come with us.
8. I am waiting for his (*ou* her) friends to arrive.
9. They can't stand being touched.
10. His parents will not (*ou* won't) let him go.

260 1. They pretend not to see me.
2. It is no use telling me how it works.
3. I don't mind not going there.
4. It didn't stop raining (*ou* it never stopped raining).
5. I heard her sing (*ou* singing).
6. I don't know how to tell him (*ou* her).
7. The customers intended to boycott that product.
8. Try to concentrate for a change.
9. Taking this train means travelling for fifteen hours.
10. I regret not mentioning it.

25 Les propositions causatives et résultatives

261 1. I'll get 2. He made 3. I'll have 4. I had 5. She made (*ou* had) 6. I'll have (*ou* make) 7. I'll get 8. makes me 9. You'll make 10. I had

262 1. I had my bedroom painted by my brother (*ou* I got my brother to paint my bedroom).
2. Fry the fish in a little oil.
3. I was made to open my suitcase.
4. Don't worry, I'll get a policeman to help you.

5. Did I make myself understood?
6. I tried in vain to make myself obeyed.
7. He had his watch stolen.
8. The traffic was very heavy and the result was that I arrived late (*très soutenu* : this led to my arriving late).
9. The thought made him smile.
10. They made me drink vodka.

263 1. I managed to get him (*ou* her) to clear up his (*ou* her) mess.
2. Mum has sent for the doctor.
3. I'll let you know as soon as I can.
4. At last, I've had my car repaired.
5. They've had their hair cut.
6. Poor things, they've been had by their lawyer.
7. All these beautiful stories make us dream.
8. The prince had the castle rebuilt.
9. As a child, my father made me make my bed every morning.
10. Don't try to make me believe that he's here.

264 1. She has washed her car clean. *Elle a lavé sa voiture, qui est maintenant propre.*
2. Jo shouted herself hoarse last night. *À force de crier hier soir, Jo s'est enrouée.*
3. Steve read himself almost blind. *À force de lire, Steve est presque devenu aveugle.*
4. She ran quickly out of the shop. *Elle sortit du magasin en courant.*
5. They starved to death. *Ils sont morts de faim.*
6. They starved themselves to death. *Ils se sont laissé mourir de faim.*

265 1. They blackmailed her **into resigning**.
2. They threatened her **into signing** the document. 3. My mother tricked me **into picking up** my aunt at the airport. 4. Erwin talked Sue **out of accepting** (*ou* **into not accepting**) the offer. 5. The President clearly fooled the State Secretary **into supporting** the resolution. 6. Sheila argued Betsy **out of becoming** (*ou* **into not becoming**) a nurse. 7. His parents begged him **not to marry** the girl. 8. My dad persuaded me **to do** a degree in maths.

26 La coordination et la subordination

266 1. She's both a mayor and a minister.
2. They can neither read nor write.
3. Either you stay and you listen to me or you go and you can do whatever you like.
4. Not only was I right but all the others were wrong.
5. If you call and (if) I'm not here, leave a message.

267 wheat <u>and</u> wine • the wheat and wine route (from north to south) <u>and</u> the salt and silver route (from west to east) • salt <u>and</u> silver • the Duke's son held out against attacks for more than a month, <u>but</u> the castle was finally pillaged and burnt • pillaged <u>and</u> burnt • the Prince of Mornmouth <u>and</u> his young and beautiful wife • young <u>and</u> beautiful • (<u>either</u>) restore it <u>or</u> build a new one (*coordonnant en deux parties :* either … or) • that he would restore it <u>but</u> that he would do it slowly and meticulously • slowly <u>and</u> meticulously • ten <u>or</u> fifteen • he <u>and</u> the Prince.

268 Dear john,
I suppose <u>that you'll be using my bedroom</u> *(sub. 1)* <u>while you're in London</u> *(sub. 2 dépendante de sub. 1)*. I'm afraid <u>I've lost the key to the large cabinet</u> *(sub. 1)* <u>that is next to the bed</u> *(relative incluse dans sub. 1)*. So <u>if you have anything confidential</u> you should keep it under the carpet, <u>as no one will think of looking there.</u> You can use my books, <u>which are all in my bedroom</u> *(relative)*, <u>though I'd appreciate</u> *(sub. 1)* <u>if you wouldn't lend them to anyone</u> *(sub. 2 dépendante de sub. 1)*, <u>as books are rarely returned</u> *(sub. 3 dépendante de sub. 2)*. I have been told by Carey, <u>who came round last night</u> *(relative)*, <u>that you intend</u> *(sub. 1)* <u>to give a party during your stay in London</u> *(sub. 2 dépendante de sub. 1)*. It's all right with me but make sure <u>that nothing gets broken</u> and <u>that everything stays clean</u> *(sub. coordonnée à la sub. précédente)*. You know <u>I hate</u> *(sub. 1)* <u>coming back to a dirty house</u> *(sub. 2 dépendante de sub. 1)*.

27 Les subordonnées relatives

269 <u>The Duke</u>, **who** … • <u>the castle</u>, **which** … • <u>the wheat and wine route</u> (**which** …) • <u>salt and silver route</u> (**which** …) • <u>his son</u>, **who** … • attacks **which** … • <u>the castle</u> **whose** walls … • <u>the town of Rigmarole</u>, **which** … • <u>an architect</u>, **whom** … • <u>The roof</u>, **whose** tiles …

270 <u>The Duke</u>, **who** : humain, pronom relatif sujet
<u>the castle</u> **which** : non humain, pronom relatif sujet
<u>the wheat and wine route</u> (**which**) : non humain, pronom relatif sujet
<u>the salt and silver route</u> (**which**) : non humain, pronom relatif sujet
<u>his son</u> **who** : humain, pronom relatif sujet
attacks **which** : non humain, pronom relatif sujet
<u>the castle</u> **whose** walls : non humain, pronom relatif génitif
<u>the town of Rigmarole</u>, **which** : non humain, pronom relatif sujet
<u>an architect</u>, **whom** : humain, pronom relatif complément
<u>The roof</u>, **whose** tiles : non humain, pronom relatif génitif

271 1. My mother, **who** was a relatively aggressive person, pushed her neighbour roughly forward. 2. We lived in a street **which** (*ou* that) contained a garage called Ever-Ready. 3. We lived in a street **whose** name was Langdon Park Road. 4. It was a narrow room **which** (*ou* that) had two windows between two wings of the building. 5. Once in a while she appeared with something **that** took you by surprise. 6. My uncle, **who** had never married, was always generous. 7. The house (that) we live in (*ou* in **which** we live) is old. 8. The man, **whose** photograph is in my wallet, was on television last night. 9. Brian, **who** is a police inspector, asked me a lot of questions. 10. The shop towards **which** I'm walking (*ou* [that] I'm walking towards) belongs to my husband.

272 1. with **whom** 2. Ø (*ou* who; *soutenu* : whom) 3. **who** 4. Ø (*ou* that ; *plus rare* : which) – and **which** 5. none of **which** 6. **whose** 7. Ø (*ou* that) 8. **that** 9. **whose** – **which** 10. **which**

273 1. Pronom relatif : *that* – proposition relative : *that women use regulary*. – antécédent : *the same*

2. Pronom relatif : *that* – proposition relative : *that has been worn and worn for many winters*. – antécédent : *some old dress*

3. Pronom relatif : *who* – proposition relative : *who no longer wanted to live with him*. – antécédent : *the woman*

4. Pronom relatif : *which* – proposition relative : *which she had received as Christmas presents*. – antécédent : *two novels*

5. Pronom relatif : *that* – proposition relative : *that she actually lived with*. – antécédent : *one*

6. Pronom relatif : *that* – proposition relative : *that dated from 1920s*. – antécédent : *records*

7. Pronom relatif : *who* – proposition relative : *who had a job in a coffee shop*. – antécédent : *a poet*

8. Pronom relatif : *whom* – proposition relative : *whom we barely remembered* – antécédent : *a man*. – pronom relatif : *whose* – proposition relative : *whose name was never mentioned*. – antécédent : *a man*

274 1. This is the person who I think would be a good candidate.

2. I don't like the way he drives at all.

3. What can we do with these books that nobody wants?

4. This museum owns many paintings, only one of which is from the twentieth century.

5. The story, which I remember very well, is less interesting than the style.

6. She owns several cars, only one of which can be used (*ou* is in working order).

7. What I realize is that it is never too late.

8. What I am proud of is my accent.

9. He's bought a house that is old but the roof of which (*ou* but whose roof) is brand new.

10. The friends I'm telling you about do not live here.

275 Dans ces phrases, l'antécédent est une proposition (*He became a drug addict – That was the end of my third section – You've always loved him – My boyfriend has been offered a new job*) et non un nom ou un groupe nominal.

Traductions de **which**
1. ce qui 2. ce qui 3. ce que 4. ce qui

276 1. What I regret is that he didn't tell me about it.

2. Ruth has always refused to tell me about it, which I regret.

3. What she told me is none of your business.

4. What they want is to be left alone.

5. Can you see what's over there?

6. What is regrettable is that he is not (*ou* he should not be) aware of it.

7. Go and see them? That's precisely what I refuse (to do).

8. They all left before the end of the match, which is really incredible.

9. What you need is a new watch.

10. He arrived with (*ou* in) what looked like a car.

277 1. Whoever loves me is to come with me.

2. I'll go wherever you go.

3. We can go whenever you want.

4. Whoever can do this exercise has understood it all.

5. He is never pleased, wherever we eat (*ou* wherever we may eat *ou* whatever the place where we eat may be).

6. Of all these cars you can choose whichever (one) you prefer.

7. We'll do whatever you want (us to do).

8. Whichever (one) of you finds the right solution first will be entitled to my respect.

28 Les subordonnées nominales en V-*ing*

278 1. Melvin('s) being late annoyed Michael.
2. Henry('s) passing his exam rejoiced his parents.
3. My failing my exam did not sadden my boyfriend.
4. Their hesitating could have been danger-ous.
5. Her ringing five minutes after the accident puzzled the policeman.
6. His leaving a note didn't make things easier.

Dans la phrase 4 : For them to hesitate could have been dangerous.

279 1. Le fait que Melvin soit en retard a agacé Michael.
2. Le fait que Henry ait réussi ses examens a fait plaisir à ses parents.
3. Mon échec à l'examen n'a pas attristé mon petit ami.
4. Leur hésitation aurait pu être dangereuse.
5. Le fait qu'elle ait téléphoné cinq minutes après l'accident a intrigué le policier.
6. Le fait qu'il ait laissé un message n'a rien arrangé.

280 1. Do you mind my (*oral :* me) leaving right now? 2. Jane remembers writing a letter of complaint to her boss. (*avec her writing, le sujet de writing serait différent de celui de* remembers). 3. He left without saying goodbye. 4. After failing to convince the prime minister, the minister decided to resign. 5. Thank you for listening with so much interest. 6. I don't object to you (*ou* your) smoking in here. 7. My students are used to travelling a lot. 8. I prefer his new habit to him (*ou* his) waking up very late. 9. We all look forward to Errol('s) visiting us soon. 10. They were busy repairing their old car.

29 Les subordonnées conjonctives

281 1. knew Ø it 2. said Ø you 3. told me Ø he – that we 4. Ø 5. that he 6. him Ø you 7. that the suspect 8. believe Ø he 9. thought Ø you 10. said that

282 1. She finds it strange that he shouldn't have phoned (*plus oral :* that he didn't phone).
2. I find it worrying that she shouldn't answer (*oral :* that she doesn't answer).
3. Do you find it normal that they should have left (*oral :* that they left) so fast?

> L'emploi de should *dans ces phrases est britannique.*

283 1. They complained that people didn't listen to them.
2. I doubt (if) I can answer you.
3. They say they want to help you.
4. I think I'll go to Edinburg tomorrow.
5. You think you'll get away with it just like that?
6. I admit that I don't know how to do it.

284 1. That he should only arrive tomor-row is surprising (*plus oral :* That he's only arriving).
2. That it should only rain once a year (*ou* rain only once a year) here seems strange to me (*oral :* That it only rains…).
3. That he should hold it against me is nor-mal (*oral :* That he holds it).
4. That she shouldn't be able to (*ou* she can't) make up her mind is understandable.
5. That he shouldn't have phoned (*ou* that he didn't phone) worries me.
6. That they should have liked (*ou* That they liked) Wagner is not that easy to under-stand.

> Les structures en it is *sont bien plus fré-quentes* : It is surprising that he should only arrive tomorrow (*oral :* that he is only arriving).

285 1. He'll regret it all the more as some day I'll be rich.
2. I don't know how she is. All the more so since she doesn't write to me any more.

3. It's all the more dangerous as you can't drive.

4. This test is all the easier for Sean as it is in English.

286 1. that she should start (*ou* that she start – *oral*: that she starts) 2. that she should be (*oral*: that she is) 3. that they should be (*ou* that they be – *oral*: that they are) 4. that we should go (*ou* that we go) 5. that you should remain (*ou* that you remain) 6. we should do (*ou* we do)

▌ *L'emploi de* should *dans ces phrases est britannique.*

287 1. It's incredible that she should have said that (*ou* that she said that).

2. It's surprising that such a thing should have happened (*ou* that such a thing happened).

3. It's not normal that they should have behaved like that (*ou* that they behaved).

4. It is regrettable that you should have quarrelled (*ou* that you quarrelled).

▌ *L'emploi de* should *dans ces phrases est britannique.*

288 1. *get* – Je vous téléphonerai dès que je serai rentré.

2. *had driven* – Il a dit qu'il viendrait dès qu'il aurait reconduit Karen chez elle.

3. *breaks down* – Nous achèterons un nouveau téléviseur quand notre vieux poste tombera en panne.

4. *broke down* – Mes parents ont dit que nous achèterions un nouveau téléviseur quand notre vieux poste tomberait en panne.

5. *have finished* – Nous partirons quand tu auras terminé ton travail.

6. *want* – Nous déménageons pour Miami le mois prochain. Venez nous voir quand vous voudrez.

7. *was* – La juge a dit qu'elle inviterait la presse une fois que son enquête serait terminée.

8. *is* – Je sais qu'il arrivera (quand il sera) trop tard.

289 1. No sooner had I seen her than I stopped my car. *ou* Hardly had I seen her when I stopped my car.

2. No sooner had is started raining than we left the beach. *ou* Hardly had it started raining when we left the beach.

3. No sooner had she called than they started laughing. *ou* Hardly had she called when they started laughing.

4. No sooner had we got off the plane than we were gripped by the cold. *ou* Hardly had we got off the plane when we were gripped by the cold.

5. No sooner had I begun accelerating than my husband screamed at me. *ou* Hardly had I begun accelerating when my husband screamed at me.

290 1. If I had known, I **would not** (*ou* wouldn't) **have come**.

2. He **will not** (*ou* **won't**) **go** if it starts raining.

3. The examiners **would have cancelled** the exam if they had been told about the cheating.

4. Brenda **wouldn't have talked** to Kevin if she had known the truth.

5. If he comes with his grandparents we **will not** (*ou* **won't**) **be able to** go climbing.

6. If you arrived two days earlier you **could** meet my new girlfriend.

7. If you pass your exam I**'ll take** you to the restaurant.

8. If you ever passed your exam I **would take** you to the restaurant.

291 1. you were 2. you made 3. things had been 4. had not been 5. behave themselves 6. applied

292 1. He insisted on trying again even though he knew it was useless.

2. They looked at each other as though they had never met.

3. We'll leave as soon as it stops raining.

4. The government will negotiate if they stop striking.

5. Take my advice: don't get married until you are over 30.

6. The path runs around a corner where it turns out of sight.
7. No sooner had he met her than he offered to marry her.
8. You may borrow my car provided you bring it back with a full tank.
9. The students enjoy this novel all the more as it is easy to read.
10. You may have any of my books as long as you take good care of them.

Dans les phrases :
1. Even though he knew it was useless, he insisted on trying again. 3. As soon as it stops raining we'll leave. 4. If they stop striking the government will negotiate. 8. Provided you bring it back with a full tank, you may borrow my car. 10. As long as you take good care of them you may have any of my books.

<hr>

30 | Discours direct et discours indirect

293 1. She didn't say anything to me. 2. Unfortunately, they didn't tell their parents anything. 3. He told you lies. (say *impossible*). 4. The headmaster told the assembly that discipline should be encouraged. 5. Stop saying to everyone that you're my boyfriend! 6. They said to their best friends that they did not want to get married. 7. You keep telling the same jokes over and over again! (say *peu envisageable*) 8. Tell the teacher about it before it's too late.

294 1. He said 2. told you 3. only saying 4. told me 5. tell the truth 6. tell you 7. can say 8. she told me 9. telling me 10. say that

295 1. My mother enquired whether (*ou* if) I wanted to marry him or not. 2. She asked me if I had had a nice meal. 3. He wondered if (*ou* whether) I had lost anything. 4. She wanted to know if (*ou* whether) I was going out that night. 5. My husband asked whether (*ou* if) the children would be home for dinner. 6. The neighbour wondered if (*ou* whether) the minister had resigned yet.

296 1. She asked where I had met him. 2. She enquired when I would be back. 3. They wanted to know what he had said to me. 4. John wondered why Chris had been late. 5. They asked who had gone. 6. She wondered how it had happened. 7. The judge wanted to know where they were. 8. Their mother asked when they were coming back.

297 1. He ordered us (*ou* me) to shut up. 2. She asked us to open our books on page 43. 3. He advised us never to say we're (*ou* we were) sorry. 4. He suggested that we should go (*ou* we go) to the cinema. 5. The guest apologized that he hadn't warned us (*ou* for not warning us). 6. She told me not to lie to her. (*ou* She forbad(e) me to lie to her. *ou* She forbad(e) me from lying to her.) 7. The policeman warned us not to park our car there (*ou* warned us that we shouldn't park our car there). 8. She invited us to come round for tea.

298 Au présent
1. The children cried they wanted to go to Disneyland.
2. Mr and Mrs Litten complained that John and William never wrote to them.
3. He said apologetically that it was too late to catch the train.

Au prétérit et au *pluperfect*
4. She announced that she had met the man of her dreams the day before.
5. Her mother explained that anyway Liz had never trusted Al.
6. They insisted that if John came two days earlier it would make things simpler.

Au *present perfect*
7. The boy said he had come to say goodbye.
8. The President's wife cried that she had decided to get a divorce.
9. The station master told Kirstie that he was sorry but that she had just missed her train.

Renvoi à l'avenir
10. The secretary explained that Mr Byrd would be here (*ou* there) in a moment.
11. Her former husband exclaimed that he would not speak to her.

12. The clairvoyant predicted that things would get better.

Modaux

13. Mother told Thomas he must (*ou* had to) come in at once.

14. Michele bragged that she could swim that length in 30 seconds.

15. The headmaster shrieked that we could stand up when he came in.

299 1. He asserted that he was going to New York.

2. She acknowledged that she had made a mistake.

3. He admitted that it was too late to react.

4. They confirmed that they had never been invited.

5. He answered that he would probably move to London in September.

6. She objected that she had (got) no time to lose.

7. The boss shouted to Nick that he was too stupid for the job.

8. Alex accepted that he hadn't had the courage to talk to her.

300 Nathalie asked Henry if he had found anyone who could help her. Henry replied that he had found a priest who would be able to help her. His name is (*ou* was) Father McCrory. He told her to go to him. Father McCrory might be able to tell her something. Nathalie thanked Henry and said that she supposed that would help. Henry asked her if she had any relatives around here (*ou* there). She answered she only had an aunt. He exclaimed that that helped a bit. She then said her aunt had had the house in Langdon Park Road. Henry said that anyway he felt sure Father McCrory could help her. He had known everybody in that neighbourhood. He advised her to try not to be too sad. One never knew. Nathalie said she knew, that life went on (*ou* goes on).

301 [...] Why had it happened to her? Did she deserve such a harsh treatment? She had always been kind to everybody and could not understand what was going on in her life. [...]

Perhaps he could not pray today because of the pain he felt. In a few days, perhaps next week, he would probably feel differently. He might even break down. That would be terrible. If he broke down, it would take weeks for him to recover…

302 Mrs Litten was feeding the fire. Tears rose to her eyes. She asked herself: "Why has it happened to me? Do I deserve such a harsh treatment? I have always been kind to everybody and cannot understand what is going on in my life." The other women did not say a word but Mrs Litten felt their sympathy. (*ou* The other women don't say a word but I feel their sympathy.)

Annexes

303 1. afraid of 2. angry with (*ou* at) 3. annoyed with 4. ashamed of 5. aware of 6. bad at – good at 7. bored with 8. close to 9. crazy about 10. disappointed with

304 1. famous for 2. fond of 3. full of 4. furious with – furious about 5. glad about 6. interested in 7. jealous of 8. kind to 9. nice to 10. pleased with/satisfied with

305 1. proud of 2. sorry about 3. surprised about (*ou* at) 4. tired of 5. worried about 6. amazed at (*ou* by) 7. annoyed with 8. worried about 9. busy with 10. clever at

306 1. delighted at (*ou* with) 2. dependent on 3. different from 4. disgusted at (*ou* by *ou* with) 5. excited about (*ou* by) 6. familiar with 7. fed up with 8. frightened of

307 1. grateful to you for telling 2. impressed with (*ou* by) 3. keen on 4. mad at (*ou* with) 5. mad about 6. responsible for – rude to – scared of – sick of 7. terrible at 8. typical of 9. upset about

308 1. think of 2. go to 3. suffers from 4. hide… from 5. escape from 6. apologize for 7. steal… from/borrowed… from 8. separates… from 9. take part in/participate in 10. succeed in

309 1. translate… into 2. divide… into 3. turned… into 4. made of 5. depend on 6. live on 7. spend… on 8. congratulate… on 9. Fill… with 10. cover… with

310 1. looking for 2. laughing at 3. approve of 4. pay for 5. comment on (*ou* upon)

311 1. What did you reply with? 2. Where did you go last summer? *(pas de préposition avec* go *interrogatif)* 3. What did she kill him with? 4. Who are you in love with? 5. Who are you dependent on? 6. Whose house did you sleep in? 7. Who is he married to? 8. Which story did you feel more interested in?

312 1. This is a (*ou* the) book (that) John is keen on.
2. I wrote a story (that) no one is interested in.
3. She is my cousin (who) I have often told you about.
4. They are friends (who) we depend on for food.
5. They are former schoolchildren (who) we are so proud of.
6. Here is a (*ou* the) house (that) the three men broke into.
7. These are rare books (that) I've been looking for everywhere.
8. The Smiths are our neighbours (who) passers-by keep looking at.

> *Dans les phrases 3, 4, 5 et 8, on aurait pu employer* whom *dans un style soutenu.* Which *aurait pu être utilisé à la place de* that *dans les autres phrases.*

313 1. The dog brought Peter two bones *ou* two bones to Peter.
2. The magician showed his partner the hat *ou* the hat to his partner.
3. My parents sent me a letter and I left Anny a message *ou* a message for Anny.
4. She wants to book Bob a plane ticket *ou* a plane ticket for Bob.
5. I'll teach her maths and she'll pay me for it.
6. The manager explained the problem to his employees.
7. We'll provide them with enough food.
8. The murderer described his act to the jury.
9. I'd like to remind my friends of the presents I gave them.
10. There is no need to ask him for his help.

314 *à travers* : across/through • *au-dessus de* : over/above • *le long de* : along • *derrière* : behind • *parmi* : among • *au-dessous de* : below • *près de* : close to/near/by • *en bas de* : down • *à l'intérieur de* : inside • *à côté de* : next to • *au large de/séparé de* : off • *en face de* : opposite • *devant* : in front of • *autour de* : round (*ou* US around) • *vers* : towards

315 1. across that street 2. across the lake 3. through the forest 4. across the blackboard 5. through New York 6. across the river 7. through the large window 8. across the hall 9. through Mary's hair 10. through a red light

316 1. at a party – in the street 2. at the bus stop 3. at the factory 4. at work – at home 5. at school 6. in Canada – in Montreal 7. in the end 8. in the country – in town 9. in the garden – at the swimming pool 10. at the end

317 1. to the pub 2. into the room 3. on(to) the floor 4. in the living room 5. into the fire 6. on(to) the platform 7. into 8. on(to) the table

318 1. between Dover and 2. between five to 3. Among those 4. among them (between them : *deux personnes*) 5. between his wife and 6. among all 7. Between you and 8. between youth and

319 1. at 3:15 2. on Christmas 3. on (*ou* Ø) Wednesday – Ø 4. at Easter – on the 5. at (*ou* on) weekends – in the evening 6. On her arrival 7. in a few days – on (*ou* Ø) Monday week 8. in three months – in August 9. on time – in the morning 10. in the afternoon – at night

320 1. I'll be waiting for you from 3 to 4. 2. Can you finish this work by tomorrow? 3. What were you doing during the summer? 4. I didn't work from June to September. 5. Call me tonight by 6 o'clock. 6. I have been at university since last year. 7. He didn't write to us for five years. 8. I have been seeing her regularly for three years.

321 1. Stop dawdling, because of you we may never be in time for our appointment. 2. Due to a late arrival of the train, the express to London will leave at 10:05. 3. Unlike Ruth I've always liked going to the pub. 4. Given their children's reluctance they decided not to go to New Zealand. 5. Considering what Brenda said we'd better not count on her.

6. Owing to the heatwave the sports event was cancelled.

322 1. Why don't you go out for a walk instead of wasting your time watching TV? 2. They decided to go on foot in spite of the weather conditions. 3. We managed to go to New York thanks to Patty's generosity. 4. What you have done is contrary to the headmaster's orders. 5. The meeting was postponed on account of their being late. 6. She failed despite her parents' encouragement.

323 1. like an idiot 2. As a teenager 3. As a professional adviser 4. like a child 5. like a dream 6. like a glove 7. as an accountant 8. like a fish 9. like that 10. like rain

324 1. on foot 2. on television 3. on strike 4. on this side of 5. on the dole (*américain :* on welfare) 6. on the third floor (*américain :* on the fourth floor) 7. in the snow 8. on fire 9. by train 10. on the plane

325 **In my opinion** singing **in the rain** is a bad habit.

If you sing alone **in the street** or **at work** people will think you're strange. **For example**, the other day I wanted to go home **on foot** rather than **by bus**. I live **in the suburbs,** five kilometres **from the city centre**. I was not **in a hurry**. I just had to be (at) home **by eight o'clock**. I felt like I was **on holiday**. As I was walking **through the park** which is **opposite the town hall**, I started singing an operatic aria. Everybody was looking me up and down. They were even turning round as I went by. **In the end**, I had to stop, so **scared** was I **of** these people.

To me it sets a **limit to** my freedom. All the more so as I have a beautiful voice. I've been taking singing lessons **for sixteen years, in fact since my childhood. As a child**, I wanted to sing **as a tenor, like Pavarotti**. True, **I'm far from it** (*ou* I'm not nearly there), **despite all my efforts**. But **between you and me**, does it really matter?

When we are **among friends**, it does not matter. By the way I am ready, my dear colleague, **to sing to you** the great tenor aria **from** *Turandot*, just **for you**. What do you mean "Out of the question"? You don't want to **listen to me**? It's **because of people like you** that freedom is trampled. I'd be better off **on a desert island** than **among** ignorant people. **At Easter**, that is **in two months**, I'll tender my resignation. I'd rather be **on the dole** than with you all. **On your arrival in September** I thought you were better than the others. How wrong I was!

32 Les adverbes

326 1. Quite frankly, I have other things to worry about. *(frankly modifie la phrase et quite modifie frankly)*
2. You're too good to be true. *(modifie l'adjectif good)*
3. Honestly I didn't say anything against you. *(modifie la phrase entière)*
4. I'll always love you. *(modifie le verbe)*
5. This film is incredibly long and dull. *(modifie les adjectifs coordonnés long and dull)*
6. He's still looking for his keys. *(modifie le verbe)*
7. I read it quite recently. *(recently modifie la phrase et quite modifie recently)*
8. He expressed his opinion convincingly. *(modifie le verbe)*

327 1. He is often away.
2. She does not always answer her mail.
3. I'll never write to them.
4. It hardly ever rains here.
5. He's always complaining about the service.
6. We've really enjoyed the show.
7. It can't possibly be true.
8. I certainly will./I certainly will not.

328 1. No sooner had she opened her mouth than I recognized her voice.
2. Never before had they seen such a beautiful show.

3. Hardly had he said a few words when he began crying.
4. No sooner had the children closed their eyes than they fell asleep.

329 1. We've all decided to move to Chicago.
2. They are all lodging a complaint against their boss.
3. We are both properly married.
4. They have each of them returned to their parents' home.
5. We will all write soon.
6. They can both be quite tiresome.
7. We each had cucumber sandwiches for lunch.
8. ... "We all are."

330 1. He explained his role unexpectedly.
2. She sang her aria well.
3. They answered angrily.
4. If you've already seen that film, we can see another one.
5. It's beautifully (*ou* nicely) said.
6. Suddenly it started raining (*ou* It started raining suddenly).
7. I'll soon go and see her in Glasgow.
8. He finally passed away at the age of 92.
9. If you go upstairs don't forget to switch off the light.
10. When did you last talk to the victim?

331 1. still love 2. boss yet 3. still 4. anything yet 5. still won't 6. that letter yet

332 1. He hasn't bought his new car yet.
2. The baby still doesn't talk. 3. I think they are still in bed. 4. Jonathan hasn't finished his work yet. 5. The defendant hasn't spoken yet. 6. The defendant is still not speaking.

333 1. Only one or two of the club women had called on her.
2. Mrs Briggs always believed in keeping her distance, too.
3. Has she ever been to Denmark?
4. They are not often ready on time.
5. On Sunday evenings she sometimes went to a lecture on philosophy.
6. You can just never tell when he is happy.

7. He had never seen Mrs Briggs so generous before.
8. It's the worst concert I've ever heard.
9. It doesn't often rain here.
10. … "No, I never have."

334 1. It's a little better. 2. I think Ives is a little drunk. 3. They really liked it (*ou* It really appealed to them). 4. This place is so much better now. 5. Look! It's been snowing a little. 6. I hardly talked to them. 7. Almost (*ou* Nearly) 80,000 people attended this concert. 8. I'm not rich enough to be able to afford this hotel. 9. I'm not really hungry. I'm really not hungry. 10. She almost felt like resigning.

335 1. Unfortunately I'm not nearly finished (*ou* I'm far from having finished). 2. I barely (*ou* hardly *ou* scarcely) counted twenty people. 3. My young brother can hardly talk, let alone write. 4. It was even hotter than last year. 5. It's a rather rich country (*ou* it's rather a rich country). 6. They are rather (*ou* pretty *ou* fairly) lazy. 7. I don't even want to talk to him (*ou* her) on the phone. 8. Even Kevin wouldn't agree with you.

336 1. Don't walk so fast.
2. This book is far too difficult to read.
3. He eats so much. He eats too much.
4. He is a far too dangerous neighbour (*ou* he is far too dangerous a neighbour).
5. He has eaten so much that it has made him ill.
6. I have (got) too much to do, I'm overworked.
7. It's too much. I won't be able to eat it all.
8. It's so clean that we no longer want to use it.

337 1. They also speak German and Italian.
2. What else could we do?
3. I too want to be a musician (*ou* I want to be a musician too).
4. We also have laptop computers if you want.
5. Anything else for you, Madam?
6. Also, we are not allowed to sell them.
7. She not only plays well, but also composes music. (*ou* Not only does she play well but she also composes music.)
8. My alarm clock didn't go off. Also, I had trouble starting the car.

338 1. Tom ne se sentait pas bien, mais il est quand même allé travailler. Cependant il n'a pas réussi à se concentrer.
2. Je n'ai jamais aimé Harry et pourtant j'ai décidé de l'aider.
3. Je sais que tu n'aimes pas recevoir des invités. Néanmoins, tu pourrais faire un effort.
4. Arrête de tricher, autrement je te dénoncerai.
5. En fait (*ou* À vrai dire), je ne peux pas te parler maintenant. Je te rappellerai.
6. « Ne t'en fais pas, on y arrivera d'une manière ou d'une autre. — Je ne sais pas pourquoi, mais j'en doute. »
7. Ces chiffres ne prouvent rien. D'ailleurs, qui les a calculés ?
8. Nous avons de plus en plus de clients et c'est pourquoi il nous faut davantage d'ouvriers.
9. C'est la fille aînée et donc l'héritière du titre.
10. Ce n'est pas très utile. C'est beau, pourtant, non ?

339 1. probably (*ou* presumably)
2. frankly
3. arguably
4. most certainly (*ou* assuredly)
5. maybe (*ou* perhaps)
6. fortunately
7. undoubtedly
8. personally
9. hopefully
10. surely
11. of course
12. admittedly
13. obviously
14. surprisingly
15. certainly
16. clearly (*ou* evidently)
17. probably (*ou* very likely)
18. naturally

340 counter-clockwise *(dans le sens inverse des aiguilles d'une montre)* • asymmetry *(asymétrie)* • incoherence *(incohérence)* • re-evaluate *(réévaluer)* • forearm *(avant-bras)* • disconnected *(débranché)* • undo *(défaire)* • irreproachable *(irréprochable)* • mistrust *(méfiance, se méfier de)* • amoral *(amoral)* • foreground *(premier plan)* • illegal *(illégal)* • forecast *(prévisions, prévoir)* • rebuild *(reconstruire)* • misspell *(mal orthographier)* • undoubtedly *(indubitablement)* • immature *(immature)* • non-smoker *(non fumeur)* • ex-husband *(ex-mari)*

341 waitress • nom formé du nom *waiter*, lui-même formé sur *wait* (servir) + suffixe *-ess* (du féminin) : serveuse

boyhood • nom formé du nom *boy* + suffixe *-hood* (du statut) : enfance

stardom • nom formé du nom *star* + suffixe *-dom* (de la condition) : célébrité

useful • adjectif formé du nom *use* + suffixe *-ful* (qui a les qualités de...) : utile

sadden • verbe formé de l'adjectif *sad* + suffixe *-en* (pour former des verbes) : attrister

driver • nom formé du verbe *drive* + suffixe *-er* (agent) : conducteur

hairy • adjectif formé du nom *hair* + suffixe *-y* (pour former des adjectifs) : poilu, chevelu

refusal • nom formé du verbe *refuse* + suffixe *-al* (action de) : refus

friendliness • nom formé de l'adjectif *friendly* (*friend* + *ly*) + *-ness* (condition) : gentillesse

catastrophic • adjectif formé du nom *catastrophe* + suffixe *-ic* (pour former des adjectifs) : catastrophique

childless • adjectif formé du nom *child* + suffixe *-less* (qui exprime une absence de) : sans enfants

foolish • adjectif formé du nom *fool* + suffixe *-ish* (qualités négatives) : stupide

laughable • adjectif formé du verbe *laugh* + suffixe *-able* (que l'on peut...) : ridicule

strangely • adverbe formé de l'adjectif *strange* + suffixe *-ly* (pour former des adverbes) : étrangement

violonist • nom formé du nom *violin* + suffixe *-ist* (agent) : violoniste

Catholicism • nom formé de l'adjectif *Catholic* + suffixe *-ism* (comportement) : catholicisme

backwards • adverbe formé de l'adverbe *back* + suffixe *-wards* (en direction de) : en arrière

childlike • adjectif formé du nom *child* + suffixe *-like* (comme) : enfantin

popularize • verbe formé de l'adjectif *popular* + suffixe *-ize* (rendre) : populariser/vulgariser

symbolical • adjectif formé du nom *symbol* + suffixe *-ical* (pour former des adjectifs) : symbolique

342 (adj. : adjectif – v. : verbe)

underpaid (adj.) • particule *under* (sous) + participe passé adjectivé de *pay* : sous-payé

undercooked (adj.) • particule *under* + participe passé adjectivé de *cook* : pas assez cuit

outrun (v.) • particule *out* (dépassement) + verbe *run* : distancer, dépasser

overeat (v.) • particule *over* (excès) + verbe *eat* : trop manger

overdressed (participe passé) • particule *over* + participe passé de *dress* : trop (bien) habillé

upgrade (v.) • particule *up* (vers le haut) + verbe *grade* : améliorer, mettre à jour

outgrow (v.) • particule *out* + verbe *grow* : devenir trop grand pour

uplifting (adj.) • particule *up* + verbe *lift* + suffixe *-ing* : édifiant, inspirant

overreact (v.) • particule *over* + verbe *act* : réagir de manière exagérée

overlap (v.) • particule *over* + verbe *lap* : se chevaucher

underrate (v.) • particule *under* + verbe *rate* : sous-estimer

overrate (v.) • particule *over* + verbe *rate* : surestimer

outdistance (v.) • particule *out* + verbe *distance* : distancer

upstage (v.) • particule *up* + verbe *stage* : éclipser, souffler la vedette à

343 Le verbe *out-Herod* est formé sur le nom *Herod* (Hérode, personnage de la Bible responsable du massacre des Innocents) et la particule *out*, qui exprime un dépassement. L'expression, créée par Shakespeare, signifie donc littéralement « être plus Hérode qu'Hérode », c'est-à-dire le dépasser en cruauté. Elle traduit parfois la tournure française « être plus royaliste que le roi ».

Achevé d'imprimer en Espagne par Macrolibros.
Dépôt légal : 93450-6/11 - avril 2018